KU-048-351

TOP SECRET FILE

Title *The Goodies File*

This book was produced by George Weidenfeld & Nicolson Ltd.

Published by Sphere Books Ltd. 1975
30-32 Gray's Inn Road, London WC1X 8JL

Copyright Tim Brooke-Taylor, Graeme Garden and Bill Oddie, 1974

ISBN 007221 1886 4

Printed in Great Britain by Morrison & Gibb

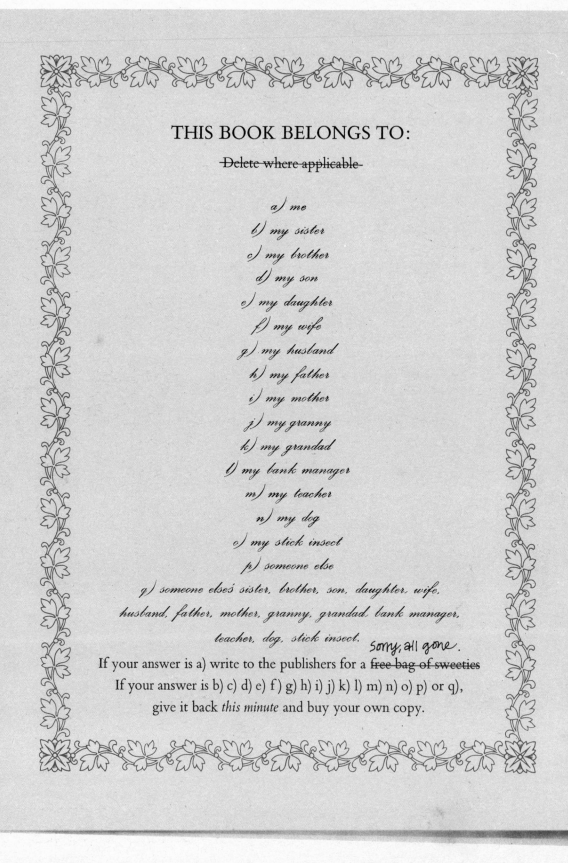

THIS BOOK BELONGS TO:

~~Delete where applicable~~

a) me

b) my sister

c) my brother

d) my son

e) my daughter

f) my wife

g) my husband

h) my father

i) my mother

j) my granny

k) my grandad

l) my bank manager

m) my teacher

n) my dog

o) my stick insect

p) someone else

q) someone else's sister, brother, son, daughter, wife, husband, father, mother, granny, grandad, bank manager, teacher, dog, stick insect.

If your answer is a) write to the publishers for a ~~free bag of sweeties~~ *Sorry, all gone.*

If your answer is b) c) d) e) f) g) h) i) j) k) l) m) n) o) p) or q), give it back *this minute* and buy your own copy.

A Message from the Publishers

We believe that this is an important book.

The documents which go to make up *The Goodies File* were brought to us by Mrs Edna Tole, one-time employee of the men in question, and now seeking to reveal to the world the activities of the growing band of secret figures who even now move among us, operating 'without the law'.

We saw at once that what we had been given was 'hot stuff' —— as our American cousins have it — but we decided (bravely perhaps) to jolly well publish and be dashed!! *That goes for us too! Basil Sphere (p.p. SPHERE PAPERBOOK BACKS)*

On reading the file, you may find it boring. More to the point, it *is* boring. Nevertheless, we felt that it was our duty to assist Mrs Tole in her ambition to expose the facts, and make a million pounds.

But let Mrs Edna Tole take up the story of how this book came to be...

397 Gallipoli Bldgs
Cherokee Way,
Cricklewood,
LONDON.

Saturday

Dear Readers,

Well, this is my first book, and I hope you all like it, tho' Norman's Janet says she is not sure, but then that's her for you.

Mr. Basil Sphere of "Sphere's" Paperbook Backs have asked me to write a Forward, so here goes!!

I first Entered the Goodies'es employment as long ago as two years ago, and since then have done for them three times a week. It was not ~~much~~ long before my suspicions were aroused regarding their activities, and I decided that enough is enough and someone must be told! Norman's Janet said no, but

Mrs Tole then goes on at some length to describe her painstaking, and often dangerous, researches — months spent sorting through waste-paper baskets, opening private letters, ransacking desks, reading diaries, and stealing things. She continues...

Blimey!!! I thought. I am holding in my hands a searing social document, as Mr. Sphere was later to put it. Well then, I will expose the Goodies'es secrets to the world, and serve the ~~buggers~~ GOODIES right, specially not having let me have had a day off when Derek was taking me over to Crawley when Norman's Janet had the operation. Not that I care/about two hoots

Eventually Mrs Tole goes on to describe how she was casually sacked by the Goodies for trying to film them in the bath, and how Norman's Janet got over the operation all right, but will never be the same again 'mark my words'.

That, briefly, is the story of how *The Goodies File* came to be put together by Mrs Edna Tole. And her reasons for doing it?...

...n *least a million pounds* but also to *show the world* that the so-called 'Goodies' (Goodies?.. Baddies more like) are *no more than a bunch of lying, thieving, swivel-eyed, two-faced,* ~~━━━━━~~, *lousy sons of*

And our reasons for publishing the book?

Much the same as hers.

This file owes its existence to the unflinching hard work of a dedicated and courageous woman. If any of you should doubt her findings, or the accuracy of her testimony, let it be said that she came to us with impeccable references...

Mrs Edna Tole

THE GOODIES

No Fixed Abode, Nr. Cricklewood, London

To whom it may concern:

re: Mrs Edna Tole.

~~This woman is a good for nothing old rat-bag.~~

Yours

The Goodies

The Goodies

Mrs Tole first entered our employment as long ago as two years ago, and has proved an honest and hard-working cleaning lady, and we have got absolutely no complaints against ~~me~~ her.

Yours

~~Edna~~ ~~Hall~~ The Goodies (Mrs)

This is true.

THEIR SECRET LIFE!
— BY EDNA TOLE (MRS)

I dont' know how you can bear
to look at these nasty pictures.
They shock me every time!

Mr Bill relaxing with his "pets"

VIRGINS REQUIRED

The three of them at
their "exclusive" club.

← Mr Jim sharing a joke with a friend.

Coots !

WE DO ANYTHING ANY TIME

Author: Bill Oddie.

Printed by: Tatty & Cheap (Prunter)

THE GOODIES ARE COMING...

WARNING by H.M. Government
GOVERNMENTS CAN
DAMAGE YOUR HEALTH

FOR YOU AND AND YOU YOU!

This is their Brochure for
~~sen~~ding to people. It is the
~~onl~~y one they've got, but
~~luc~~kily everybody sends it
~~str~~aight back.

E. J. (mrs)

PLEASE READ ON

ff 'Help! – I need somebody

Help! – Not just any body'

The Beatles* (1967)

 N THOSE WORDS Lennon and McCartney could so easily have been writing about the Goodies, but they weren't. In fact I've no idea *what* they were writing about half the time. All that rubbish about 'I am the Walrus' and Eleanor Rigby keeping her teeth in a jam jar or something, and *what* 'Lucy in the Sky with Diamonds' means I do NOT know! Still, it was better than the boring 'heavy' rubbish John's into these days or, indeed, those soppy tunes Paul sings now. Anyway – *Everybody* does need *Help* – sometime, somewhere – and The Goodies provide it – *Anytime, Anywhere*. So why not give us a call? – *Now!*

Well go on!
Oh alright then – we'll tell you *More*.

What do you get when you hire the Goodies?
Quite simply – us – three men (or two and a half) – minds, bodies, and socks – for you to do *whatever* you want with (as long as it doesn't tickle).

> **WARNING** by H.M. Government
> WINKING CAN DAMAGE
> YOUR HEALTH

*
'The Beatles' were a popular singing group in the 1960s.
Now read on . . .

NOTE: TURN EITHER THE PAGE, THE BOOK, THE ROOM OR YOUR HEAD
NINETY DEGREES FOR EASE OF READING.

WHO ARE THE GOODIES?

TIMOTHY BROOKE-TAYLOR   DR. DAVID GRAEME GARDEN   WILLIAM EDGAR ODDIE

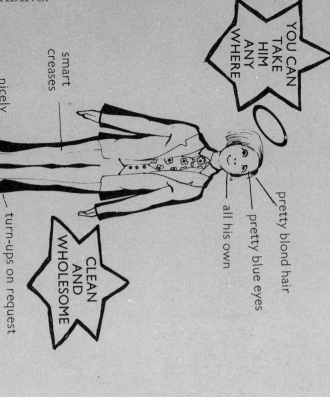

YOU CAN
TAKE
HIM
ANY
WHERE

CLEAN
AND
WHOLESOME

pretty blond hair
pretty blue eyes
all his own
smart
creases
nicely
shined
turn-ups on request

Born: Buxton, Derbyshire, 1940
Age: 23+
Height: Just right. Weight: Perfect.
Specialities:
Very good at making a speech (usually the same one). *Always* wears a tie (especially in the bath), has own suit, and speaks posh. Impersonates ladies (has own dresses, bras, knicks etc). *But* is nevertheless extremely Butch (considering he's so pretty). If you call at our office, Tim is the one who will speak nicely to you, shake your hand, lick your boots, etc, etc . . .

optional
brown
brown
brown
brown
brown
brown
brown

Born – (Invented), Scotland.
Age: Looks older than he is.
Height: The tallest. Weight: skinny.
Specialities:
Wears glasses, which means he is extremely clever and short-sighted. To be perfectly honest, he is a *Swot*. Will *Never* use one word when ten will be more confusing. When excited, jabbers like a Gibbon. All in all, if you want to blind anyone with science – Graeme's your man. Impersonates almost everybody, especially Eddie Waring. If you call at our office, Graeme is the one who will be so busy reading, he won't even notice.

RENT
A
SCRUFF

greeny brown
purple
yellow
cream
(makes you
throw up-
doesn't it!).

Born: Unfortunately, Rochdale, 1941.
Age: Work it out, if you *must* know.
Height: Not much. Weight: Variable.
Specialtitties:
Difficult to single out any one of Bill's qualities – largely because he hasn't really got any. Used to be fat, and was very cozy to sit on. Now not so fat, but being sat on is still probably his best use. Very good at frightening people away. Also sings (which frightens people away). Hairy. Impersonates Old English Sheep dogs. If you call at our office Bill is the one who will bite your ankles. (For an extra fee he can be left..ocked up in his box.)

WARNING by H.M. Government

OU

CHOICE

RE

 "That *tort-ure* a lesson!" Here's Goody Oddie being cross examined (and he's cross alright) as he *racks* his brains to find a way out. But did Bill *crack*? No! Even though he stretched a bit! *Ouch!*

And here's The Goodies *jockee-ing* for position against the dreaded bagpipe spider – and they certainly taught him a *fling* or two!!

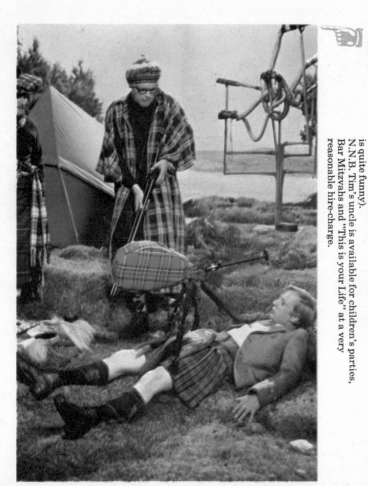

*N.B. THE GOODIES wish to thank the script-writer of "SCOOBY-DOO" for providing the captions on this page. THE GOODIES also wish to apologise for the picture of Tim's uncle, which has nothing to do with our past exploits, and has got in by mistake (even if it is quite funny).
N.N.B. Tim's uncle is available for children's parties, Bar Mitzvahs and "This is your Life" at a very reasonable hire-charge.

ST

UNIQUE

RD

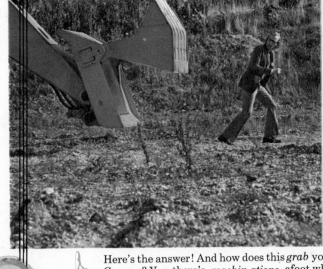

Here's the answer! And how does this *grab* you Graeme? Yes, there's *machin-ations* afoot when the beastly bulldozers try to take over the world. But when those monster earth movers come up against The Goodies, well, it's a building *site* for sore eyes! Can you *dig* it?

But what's this? Tim *hanging* around on the job? Not likely, he's just *swinging* into battle, as usual. And his chums will soon get him off the *hook*. So what's he *up* to? We won't keep you in *suspense* any longer . . .

this time. Well, did you *heffer*?! Is he being taken for a *ride*? Or did he have no *udder* choice? Whoever *herd* of such a thing! In fact, here's the truth – and no more *bull* – it's not Tim at all, it's his loony uncle – better *steer* clear of *him*!

WARNING by H.M. Government
VOTING CAN DAMAGE
YOUR HEATH

AND WHAT OF THE FUTURE?

Already The Goodies have exiting NEW plans in the pipeline.
These are JUST A FEW of the thrilling endeavours they will attempt
during the coming year (probably).

Artist's Impression

Sailing around the World non-stop
(except to go to the lavatory) in
a dug-out Derby Ram

Artist's Impression

A Goodies health farm on the
Polar Ice Cap

DO NOT FEED THE LIONS

The establishment of a brand new
Safari Park in the middle of
Trafalgar Square

Artist's Impression

The first manned landing on the
Sun (leaving at night in case the
surface is too hot)

What facilities can we offer? ? ?

If you hire The Goodies you get the benefit of the use of
all these inclusive Goodies facilities – any MANY MORE (well, a few)

 **Door to Door Service –
we get there Fast**

 Our Fully Mobile Office

 **And the extensive Goodies
Wardrobe**

 **with its unequalled range of disguises –
to suit any mission.**

How Much Will It Cost?

We have always prided ourselves that we are cheaper than *Anyone Else* you will find *Anywhere*.

We regret that, with the continued deterioration of the Country's economy, we have been forced to revise our fees a little this season. We trust you will not find the increases unreason-able.

Consultation Fee: ~~50p~~ £10.00
Personal Problems: ~~50p~~ £125.00
Embarrassing Problems: ~~£1.00~~ £150.00
Very Embarrasing Problems ~~£1.25~~ £250.00
Very Difficult Problems: ~~£0.75p~~ £195.00
Impossible Problems: ~~£1.50p~~ £10,000.00
Mending Fuses: ~~£0.02p~~ £32.00

Prices do Not include VAT, tips, or danger money.

How Do You Get In Touch With Us?

Just walk round the streets, wearing a Goodies T-shirt and waving a Goodies L.P. and shouting "Goodies For Ever!" – and we'll hear you eventually.

Now – read what others say about The Goodies.

| ?? ?? | •••• | NO | o o o | npq&2 | 'Which' Magazine |

 "A rip off"
The Monkees

 "Fart oo nice"
M. Python

TRY US – NOW!
WE DO ANYTHING ANYTIME

FOR YOUR EYES ONLY
==================

CONFIDENTIAL

H.M. DEPARTMENT OF NATIONAL SECURITY
(and not Spying)

c/o MI9
13 Rotherfield Road
Welwyn Garden City
Herts.

FIRST CLASS

Top Secret

HANDS OFF!!

TO:-

The Goodies,

No fixed Abode,

London NEI9 43CW

Dear Goodies,

Just a short note to thank you for clearing up that little matter involving
the Rt. Hon. ████████████ and the goats. Your efforts were greatly
appreciated by the Government, and by Her Majesty the ████ herself.
Jolly well done!

The bally Ruskies still don't know what hit them, and the CIA chaps are
fuming! My ankle is a lot better now, and I'll be up and about in no time,
though Doctor ██████ says the Prime ██████ will have to lay off the
cello for a week or two. The sideboard wasn't too badly burned, and it
turned out that Sister Maria Theresa had a wooden leg anyway, so no
harm done. Putting the old Concordre together again may take some time,
but at least the Blackpool Tower people aren't suing for damages - they
only lost the top bit anyway. ██████ sends his regards, and hopes to
see you when they take the bandages off.
Sorry about Tim's trousers.

All the best

~~████████████~~

Head of MI9

THIS LETTER IS <u>NOT</u> TO BE READ BY SPIES. PROMISE?

found in Mr. Tim's desk
E. Tole (Mrs)

So...You think you're pretty naughty!?

1) When you see a girl, what do you look at first?
a) Her eyes ✓
b) Her hair
c) Her teeth
d) Her Satinex Rubber Body-Stocking
e) Anything else

2) What do you look at next?
a) Her hands
b) Her nose
c) Your shoes ✓
d) Her husband

3) If you want to date her, do you
a) Ask her there and then
b) Phone her
c) Write a note
d) Forget about it ✓

4) When you take her out on that oh-so-important first date, do you give her
a) Flowers ✓
b) Chocolates
c) One

5) Do you know where babies come from?
a) Yes ✓
b) No
c) Not telling

6) If you have a free evening, do you prefer to take out
a) Your wife
b) Your secretary
c) A girl friend ✓
d) Your teeth

7) What really turns you on?
a) Being tickled
b) Tickling somebody else
c) Reading poetry ✓
d) Playing whist

How do you measure up as a lover?

Tick *your* answers to these questions, then turn to page 903 for your score

8) Are you *sure* you know where babies come from?
a) Not telling ✓

9) Do you use a deodorant?
a) Yes ✓
b) No

Could have fooled me.

10) Do you believe in holding hands before marriage?
a) Yes
b) No

c) Don't understand the question ✓

11) If you think you are in love with a girl of the opposite sex, do you
a) Tell her so
b) Write poems
c) Run about with her in slow motion
d) Buy her a Satinex Rubber Body-Stocking ✓

12) Do you realise how much a Satinex Rubber Body-Stocking costs!?

a) No
b) Yes
c) Yes, but I know this little place ✓

13) How many positions do you know?
a) 1 ✓
b) 69
c) 1 *and* 69

14) Do you consider yourself one of the world's greatest lovers?
a) Yes ✓
b) Yes

15) Are you sure?
a) Well, possibly...
b) No, but you see...

16) Answer Yes or No
a) Yes
b) No
c) Well... ✓

17) YES or NO!
a) Yes ✓
b) No

18) Do you honestly expect me to believe that?
a) Yes! Yes! YES!!! ✗
b) Oh all right then, No ✓

19) No. Exactly. In fact I put it to you that you are nothing more than a disgusting evil-minded little creep
a) You cad!
b) I am undone! ✓

20) Now answer carefully, when you go to bed at night do you
a) Take a
b) Open y
c) Wear la

ANSWERS TO QU
ALL a)'s : 100%
ALL b)'s : 15%
ALL c)'s : —9.5%
(If you answered a)
question 20

LIMITED EDITION

The Goodies
Garden of Verse

A compendium of youthful poetry by

Tim Brooke-Taylor   *Graeme Garden*   *Bill Oddie*

Collected and edited by

Tim Brooke-Taylor

With an introduction by

Tim Brooke-Taylor

Published by

Soppy and Wet

London

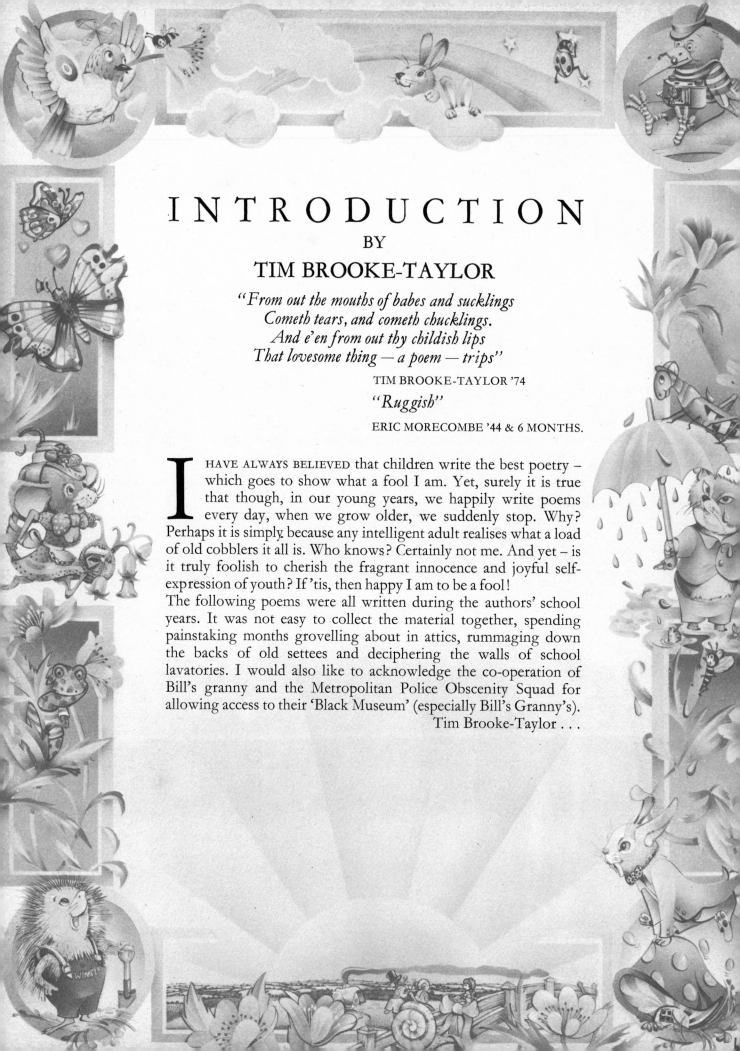

INTRODUCTION
BY
TIM BROOKE-TAYLOR

"From out the mouths of babes and sucklings
Cometh tears, and cometh chucklings.
And e'en from out thy childish lips
That lovesome thing — a poem — trips"

TIM BROOKE-TAYLOR '74

"Ruggish"

ERIC MORECOMBE '44 & 6 MONTHS.

I HAVE ALWAYS BELIEVED that children write the best poetry – which goes to show what a fool I am. Yet, surely it is true that though, in our young years, we happily write poems every day, when we grow older, we suddenly stop. Why? Perhaps it is simply because any intelligent adult realises what a load of old cobblers it all is. Who knows? Certainly not me. And yet – is it truly foolish to cherish the fragrant innocence and joyful self-expression of youth? If 'tis, then happy I am to be a fool!

The following poems were all written during the authors' school years. It was not easy to collect the material together, spending painstaking months grovelling about in attics, rummaging down the backs of old settees and deciphering the walls of school lavatories. I would also like to acknowledge the co-operation of Bill's granny and the Metropolitan Police Obscenity Squad for allowing access to their 'Black Museum' (especially Bill's Granny's).

Tim Brooke-Taylor . . .

ANIMALS

At The Zoo BY TIM BROOKE-TAYLOR, AGED 2

Someone's let the gibbon out, the gibbon's
        got away
Oh isn't it a pity – that he's not here today
I did so want to see him – wherever can he be?
I wonder if he's hiding – shall I go and see?
I'm looking here, I'm looking there,
      I just can't find him anywhere
Where is he, where IS he?
      Where can that naughty gibbon be?
I'm looking high, looking low
Where is the little so and so.
If ever he comes back again –
I'll smash his rotten teeth in!

I Wish . . . BY TIM, AGED 20

I wish I was a dicky bird
Oh! wouldn't I be sweet?
I'd fly up to the apple tree
And sing tweet tweet tweet tweet
Tweet tweet tweet tweet tweet tweet tweet
Tweet tweet tweet tweet tweet tweet tweet
          etc, etc . . .

Christopher Robin.

!!S??t! ???k!! Listen, who swears?
Christopher Robin has fallen down stairs.

Ode to 'The Tax Collector'.

Thirty five pounds 70.

Mice Pudding BY GRAEME GARDEN, AGED 12

Pies are nice
And so are mice.

My Dog BY BILL ODDIE, AGED 4

I have a dog with seven paws
With bloodshot eyes
and savage jaws
His teeth are long
and pointed
And his legs are
double jointed
And he scratches hamsters eyes out with his claws.
He's got other nasty habits,
Like chewing bunny rabbits
And he often eats a pussy cat for tea.
If you say: "it isn't true!"
I'll set my dog on you.
And he'll bite your ruddy leg off – just you see!

Buffalo BY BILL ODDIE, AGED 8

Oh give me
a home
Where the
Buffalo roam,
And I'll show
you a house
With a very messy
carpet.

LOVE

AND OTHER POEMS

The Kiss BY TIM BROOKE-TAYLOR, AGED 9

Linda Cosgrave kissed me!
It nearly made me sick
I wasn't even looking –
Oo what a beastly trick!
Her mouth was wet and greasy
And her sticky little lips
Were full of salt and vinegar –
She'd been eating fish and chips.
I told her she was "yucky",
And she went off in a huff.
If that's what kissing girls is like,
I'm going to be a puff!

SATIRE Our Leader
BY GRAEME GARDEN

William Gladstone –
What a squirt.
He wears lipstick
and a skirt.

Trousis BY GRAEME GARDEN, AGED 31

Always wear trousis
In Public Houses,
Or you'll have nowhere to put the change.

Blank Verse.
BY TIM BROOKE-TAYLOR, AGED 9

Love Is BY BILL ODDIE, AGED 16

There's a girl in 3C
With a wart on her knee
And a pimple upon her behind.
I gave her 3p
And she showed it to me
Don't you think that was awfully kind?
P.S. Wonder what she'd do for a quid!

Business Reply Service
Licence No. W.B. 96

The Reader's Digest Association Limited,
"Nobel Prize" Offer,
7-10 Old Bailey,
London EC99

No time to lose! Still time to win!

hurry! hurry! hurry! hurry! hurry! hurry! hurry! hurry!

Lucky Number: **254**

Dear **Graeme**

Great News!

You, **Graeme** may already be one of the lucky winners in this year's grand Nobel Prize draw!

Yes, your number may be the lucky one which could already have won you, **Graeme** one of the few coveted Nobel prizes!

All you need to do is send in your enclosed lucky number, and you could receive a Nobel Prize by return of post:

The envy of all your friends, and an elegant addition to your living room wall or mantelpiece, and an exciting talking point at all the parties you hold at **no fixed abode**

Just send in your lucky number, and answer these simple questions:—

1) Identify three discrepancies in Einstein's special theory of Relativity with special reference to the constant $3x/c$.

2) Define the place of Molecular Biology in a clone community.

3) Complete the following sentence:—

 "I think I should have a Nobel Prize because

Good luck!   Yours *Ron Jones.*

(This competition is not open to employees of the Nobel Dynamite Co. Ltd., or members of their families.)

Boots, Boots, Boots, Boots, Marchinup & Downagain,
Solicitors and Commissioners for Oaths.

'Bertfreda',
19 Mohammed Alley,
Gosport,
Hants.

The Goodies
No fixed abode
Near Crouch End

Date as postmark

Dear Sirs

I have been instructed by my client to communicate with you regarding
the alleged events, beginning Sunday February 16th. The aforementioned
events, as you will recall, were as follows:-

1.   On the evening in question, you did unlawfully gain entrance to
my client's premises by impersonating a six-legged pantomime Dromedary
with a silly French accent. As such, you were accepted, in good
faith, as a guest in my client's house, and even given a cup of tea
and fifteen Bakewell tarts in a nose-bag.

2.   My client, (hereinafter referred to as 'my client') had to leave
the room for a moment for urgent consultation with his business
associate, the Rev. 'Kinks' Codd.

3.   While he was out of the room, you ate the piano.

4.   On his return, my client (in a tolerant mood as he has no great
taste for music) requested an explanation. He was immediately set
upon by you, without provocation, resulting in a wilful breach of his
trousers.

5.   You then proceeded to ridicule my client (hereinafter referred to
as 'old skinnypins'.)

6.   This behaviour continued for some five or six months, until last
August, when it was brought to my client's notice that a six-legged
pantomime Dromedary, wearing his hat, had attempted to cash a cheque
for £250,000 in his name at the local off-licence. This aroused his
suspicion.

7.   On September 2nd, choosing his moment, my client informed you of
his misgivings, and requested an explanation.

8.   You ate his undergarments. (Mauve.)

9.   My client, reasonably in the circumstances, requested you to
leave his premises, which you refused to do, even when threatened with
eviction. You further claimed 'Squatters' Rights' in his home, and
applied for arbitration to the Rent Tribunal.

P.T.O.

10. My client has subsequently agreed to pay you £13 a week rent.

11. On September 23rd, my client called in the Bailiffs.

12. On September 24th the Bailiffs arrived. You joined them in a rather amusing routine which involved papering the parlour.

13. The Rev. 'Kinks' Codd was obliged to intervene on my client's behalf.

14. He was papered.

15. During the month of October, my client was obliged to be away from home during his stay at the 'Bide-a-wee' Funny Farm, Okehampton.

16. On his return, he discovered you still in residence, but was prepared to accept your explanation that you were not the <u>same</u> pantomime Dromedary, but that you were in fact the late Sarah Bernhardt.

17. My client's amateur production of 'My Fair Lady' at the Godalming Occasional Players Theatre, Wolverhampton, on October 3rd, was universally hailed as a disaster on the first night. And I quote ".... the role of Eliza Dolittle was played by the late Sarah Bernhardt like a six-legged pantomime Dromedary with a silly French accent .... (the Wolverhampton Courier)."

18. October 4th: my client consulted us to seek legal advice.

19. October 5th: we sent my client a bill for our services.

20. October 6th: the bill was paid by my client.

21. October 7th: we lost interest in the case.

And so, for the moment, the matter rests. However my client has expressed some concern regarding the current situation, and informs us that it has had some considerable effect on his previous relationship with Miss Desiree Gaspinforit (formerly the Rev 'Kinks' Codd.)

Charges are not to be pressed by us, but we look forward to your early reply regarding just compensation.

Yours

Geronimo Boots

(pp Boots Boots Boots Boots Marchinup & Downagain.)

PS - Will you please get off my desk?

THE GOODIES

No Fixed Abode, Nr. Cricklewood, London

Dear Mr. Boots,

        In reply to your letter:

1) We deny all knowledge of the events mentioned.

2) We have **never** dressed up as a pantomime dromedary - with or without a silly accent.

3) It must have been three other people - possibly the Beverly Sisters, or even the Swedish Prime Minister and two like minded friends.

4) Alternatively, have you considered the possibility that it may not have been three people in a skin, but might actually have been a real pantomime dromedary?

5) We have no intention of paying compensation.

6) and, sixthly,

7) Your client, who is known to us, should stop telling fibs and return immediately to his husband, last heard of on a camping holiday in Harlow New Town.

Your Obedient Servants,

The Goodies

following the
provisions will be in default of these matters and await also our client's instructions.
visions will be taken to see it done if we do not ---
my trouser and await also our client's instructions.
this particular time for right of the law!
has come circumstances of
a bunch of swine -

Geronimo Boots

Geronimo Boots

oh, all right forget it.

N.B.
At this point, I must point out the help and encouragement given to me in my campaign to expose the so-called Goodies by my good friend P.C. Bent of the Police Force.
Thankyou.   Edna Tole (Mrs.)
                        (This is our first exchange of letters.)

METROPOLITAN POL

Dear Mrs. Tole, (Mrs.)

Thankyou for your most <u>interesting</u> letter. The information you enclosed suggests that this case might well provide for me the promotion I so richly deserve, and for you the ~~sum of one million pounds~~ satisfaction of a job well done.

However, I think we shall need more concrete evidence. I enclose half a brick, and I should be grateful if you would "plant" it. Then — I shall <u>pounce</u>!

Don't forget though, as we say in the force — 'Softly Softly, catchee monkey!'

Yours.

P.C. Bent (P.C.)

many thanks! Let ____ ____ ____ have planted the half-brick you ____ ____ ____ sent, but so far nothing has come up — despite plenty of watering and manure. However, we must wait and see. But now the good news, I <u>have</u> caught a monkey,

P.T.O.

METROPOLITAN POLICE—CRIMINAL RECORDS DEPARTMENT

Name of Villain or Tearaway   Oddie, Bill

Name (in the right order)   Bill Oddie

Date of birth: ?

Mug Shots:

Age: 30 $\frac{1}{8}$

Sex: Male

Height: 3 ft. 6 $\frac{1}{4}$"

Colouring: Hair the colour of Jacobean stained oak. Eyes - mouse

Inside Leg: Practically none.

Educasion: Mother Goose Infant Primary (Godalming)
(Expelled for cheating.)

Mother Goose Approved Infant Primary (Isle of Wig

Open University (Escaped.)

Known Activities: Member of notorious Goodies mob.
Believed to have been involved in 'The Case of the
Chinese Box' (by Dorothy L. Sayers, £1.50p., Victor
Gollancy).

Fell ~~off bike~~ back of like in June 1971. *Personally I think it's what it's up to be, but that's my opinion. P.C. Bea~~*
Subsequently shown on 'Police 5'.

Sings:
Not much on this one I'm afraid - but we'll keep trying
(Characteristic habit, when nervous, of lightly drumming
his head against policemen.)

Other Information:

Alias: Fungus Face, Fuzzy peg, o William Oddie

Dabs:

METROPOLITAN POLICE—CRIMINAL RECORDS DEPARTMENT

Name of Villain or Tearaway Brooke - Taylor - Tim

Name (in the right order) Taylor - Tim ~~Taylor~~ ~~Tim-Brooke~~ ~~Tim Taylor~~ Tim - Brooke
Brooke - Tim Taylor

Date of birth: August 17 1893

Age: 21

Sex: ●●●● (the more blobs the better)

Height: 10 st. 5 lb.

Colouring: NONE

Inside Leg: Curiously appealing

Mug Shots:

Educasion: Mother Goose Infant Primary (Godalming)

I. Canem's Academy for the sons of gentlefolk with funny names.

The University of Life (Failed)

Public School - Winchester ('73)

Known Activities: Crochet & Needlework (has won prizes)

Member of notorious Goodie mob since 1970.
Known sympathiser with Old Age Pensioners.
Alias - Jack the lad
Sten-gun Steve
Hopalong Wilkinson R.N. (Retd.)
Winnie the Pooh.
Pooh the Winnie.
P.C. Bent.
Gladys Hazbottle
His Holiness Pope Pius II
Abdul al Rahman and his educated Dromedary

Other Information:

Henry VIII died in 1547.

this is true. P.C. Bent.

Dabs:

METROPOLITAN POLICE—CRIMINAL RECORDS DEPARTMENT

Name of Villain or Tearaway **Garden, Graeme**

Name (in the right order) **Graeme Garden**

Date of birth: Feb. 18th 1943

Age: 116   73   73
            43   -43
            116   30

Sex: ✓

Height: Average

Colouring: Average

Inside Leg: Average

Mug Shots:

Educasion: Mother Goose Infant Primary (Kirkcudbright)
~~Eton & Harrow~~ Penge.
Universities: Cambridge, Oxford, Harvard, Yale,
St. Andrews, Sussex, Solihull Poly.

Qualifications: MA., M.B., B.Chir, D.Ph., Ph.D., Dh.P., L.h.B., L.O.O

Known Activities:
NOT | Member of Goodies Mob.
    | Known as 'Brains'.
Picked up for questioning last April, and asked us many
                                        interesting questions
Arrested while in posession of £3,000,000 pounds in gold bull
and charged with possessing £3,000,000 pounds in gold bull
(acquitted).
<u>Parking offence!</u>
Charged with riding a bike without lights. (aged 3)
Personally, I myself brought him in last week - drunk and
~~dis orderly~~. But when I sobered up, he'd gone. Sorry.

Other Information:

THIS MAN IS ~~DGA~~ ~~DANJERU~~ ~~DANGEROUS~~ ~~DANGUEROS~~ ~~US~~ SAFE

Dabs:

Sorry - some of
these dabs are mine.
P.C. Bert
(sorry)

METROLOPITAN POLICE
IQ TEST

This will give you some idea of P.c. Benk's calibre! E.T. (Mrs)

Name **P. C. Bent**

What is the next number in this sequence?

2 3 4 5 6...?

23, 457

A = 1
B = 2
C = ?

C

Which is the odd man out?

...ief Inspector 'Nancy' Bottle

Bread is to butter
as knife is to *cut it with*

What have all these shapes in common?

They are all in question 5)

What does this remind you of?

A Rorschack ink-blot test.

---

7. What is the number in this circle?

I can't see one.

8. "Hey diddle, the .... and the fiddle."
What is the missing word?

Wrong! What is not the missing word. (Trick question eh??)

9. 879 + 339 =
    531 + 117 =
    864 ×   = 1,147

These sums have got some numbers missing.

10. Road   now: Down
     Read   *READ*
     Reap   *REAP*
     Heap   *HEAP*
     Help   *Burn*

11. Make up a story about the drawing you see below.

One bright morning Milly Molly Mandy set off shopping "Come on you lot" she P.T.O

COOKERY CORNER

How To Cook A Leather Armchair.

① PEEL CAREFULLY

② Remove springs....

as always, keep springs for making Soup

③ Simmer gently in 75 gallons of french otter grease for 36 years, or until tender.

④ ADD onions, shallots, parsley, and any left-over armadillo giblets...

⑤ GENTLY stir in ½ pint of cream, or if you have no cream 17¼ Poodles' eyes...

⑥ allow to stand until offensive

⑦ open a window.

⑧ ADD cushions, and garnish with live toads.

add salt to taste

CHUCK IT OUT.

THE G

Here demonstrated by Norman and Norm
Higginbottom – a bank-clerk and a
hair-stylist – from Esher (actually it's
Graeme and Tim dressed up – hoo hoo!)

THE GOODY – THE DANCE T

1 ST STEP : Imagine you are sweeping the ballroom. Sweep to the left – then to the right.

Count : 1 2 3 4 1 2 3 4 1½

2 ND STEP : It's as if you have found a lighted cigarette on the floor – you stamp your foot on it to put it out.

Count : 1 2 3 4 5 6 7 8 ⅓

3 RD STEP : BUT – it burns a hole right through the sole of your shoe and you leap in the air.

Count : 9–10

4 TH STEP : Now – as if holding your foot in your hands you hop 2 to the right – count 1 2 3 4, 2 to the left – count 5 6 7 8 – twice round the room. Count : 9 10 11 12 13 etc. to 119 – hop backwards – Count : 119, 120, Forwards 121 – 122 and fall flat on your back.

5 TH STEP : Help your partner up. Count 1 – 2. And – as if by accident – pull her over backwards.
Count : 3 4

C'MON EVERYBODY – TAKE YOUR PARTNER

IT'S NEW
✳ IT'S GROOVY ✳
IT'S AMAZINGLY
COMPLICATED

SWEEPING THE BALLROOM

8 TH STEP : Grab her in a double leg-lock with a back arm twist.

Count : 5 6 7 8

6 TH STEP : Next – kick your partner in the stomach, whilst shouting out "Clumsy git!"

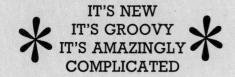

Count : 1 2

9 TH STEP : Give her a playful karate flip arm twisting neck bender – Whee !

Count : 9-10   OUT !

7 TH STEP : Let her kick you back.

Count : 3 4

10 TH STEP : Phone for a) a masseur, b) an ambulance, c) an undertaker, depending on the damage inflicted. Give yourself as LONG AS YOU NEED to recover. ORFT YOU GO AGAIN Same movements for 2nd verse – only man dances lady's steps

IT'S
AS SIMPLE
AS
THAT.

THE FLOOR – AND DO THE GOODY – WOW!

HOW TO PLAY
'Land of Hope and Glory'
on milk bottles

by Tim Brooke-Taylor

Most of us like to play
'Land of Hope and Glory' at
least three or four times a day.
However, if there isn't a gramophone,
or musical instrument handy,
I find a satisfactory rendering can be
achieved by filling 6 milk bottles
to the levels indicated below,
and producing the required notes
by striking them with a piano or
gramophone. Or even a ruler. Thus

1	2	3	4	5	6
	1"	2"	3"	4"	5"

Land	of	hope	and	glory,	mother	of the	free
5	5	3-4	5	4-3	2-2	1-2-3	1

Some of those involved!
as snapped by me.
(Edna Tole) (Mrs.)

"The Goodies"   (1/60 sec, f 11.)

Mr. Tim. (10 sec. time exp. f 22)

Mr. Bill (arrowed). (Pentax Brownie. 135mm lens.)
5.6 secs. f 1/30 Agfacolor.

'Autumn Nocturne' by E. Tole (Mrs)
(courtesy Radio Times Hulton
Picture Library.)

P/c Bent ( )

Mr. Graeme (1/200 flash
+ cloud filter.)

Chief Inspector George W. Bottle.
(indoor flash)

GOODIES THEME SONG

WORDS & MUSIC BY BILL ODDIE.
with help from Tim. and Graeme

Copyright Bill Oddie '69
Original Manuscript...

* Send copy to Engelbert, Tom, Des, Slade & Little Jim. *

GOODIES - GOODY GOODY GUM DROPS
Don't like Gum drops (T) How about LIQUORICE ALLSORTS ?! (Graeme)
BUM x BUM too rude!   TUM TUM even ruder   YUM YUM ✓

TAKE A LITTLE GOOD ADVICE   Take a little Lovely TRAM   PARADISE ?
TAKE A TRIP TO BOGNOR REGIS   Doesn't rhyme? How about WEST HAM ? rhymes / Blackburn Rovers

IT'S REALLY NOT SO HARD TO FIND
YOU'VE GOT IT IN YOUR HEAD FOOT HAND MIND ✓

IT'S WHATEVER TURNS YOU ON ← Is this a drugs reference? No! Pity.
GOODIES   GOODIES   Why?   It's whatever turns you on - opt it?   No - GOODIES
SWITCH   SWITCH

IT'S ANYTHING YOU WANT IT TO BE   To rhyme with BE please!
A suggestions?   OR A
A suggestions?   WOMBAT   PolarBear
Radioactive isotope?   RECORD   Okapi   Lady's KNEE   the BBC   fee gee   cup of tea wee wee   O.B.E ✓

A CIRCUS OR A SEASIDE PIER   PEER beer   HAPPEN
WE MAKE IT EVER SO NEAR VERY QUEER   beer dear   HERE.

FINE FOR EVER-Y BOD-Y   YOU-OO-OO- AND ME - what about me?
All THE FAMILY ?   X rubbish !
GOODIES & GOODIES   ALL THE FAMILY

GOODIES - GOODY GOODY GUM DROPS   Liquorice Allsorts   BUM BUM TUM TUM   AAAAH OO OO   YUM YUM   Yeah Baby! Too Much
GOODIES - GOODY GOODY GUM DROPS   Liquorice Allsorts   BUM BUM TUM TUM   YUM YUM   Far Out!
WE'RE COMING FOR YOU   OW EEK   UH !   No we're 1st.

ANYONE CAN RIDE ALONG - WE ARE VERY BIG & STRONG
THERE'S NOTHING THAT YOU CANNOT DO.
AND YOU'LL BE A GOODY Doo Ioo Io Ioo 2.
ALL YOU NEED'S A LITTLE LOVE - me?
ANYONE CAN SING OUR SONG. Who'd want to?
GOODIES - GOODY GOODY GUM DROPS etc
BUM BUM TUM TUM YUM YU

The Goodies

Annual Prize-Giving Dinner

Your presence is requested at a slap-up feed
at the
HOTEL DE POSH

Dress   Goodies' T-shirts and dirty jeans
Anyone wearing a tie will be thrown out

**Bring Bottle
and Raquel Welsh**

ORDER OF EVENTS

7.30 Dinner

Menu

Salt and Vinegar crisps or Scotch Broth with enormous dumplings

Eggs with Soldiers

or

Fishfingers and Baked Beans

or

Chip Butties

or

All the above, served on one plate with lots of tomato ketchup

Christmas Cake with N O Marzipan

'Pop'

Marshmallows you can pick the chocolate off

Mars Bars (to be sucked not bitten)

Sherbet Fountains

Custard Pies (not to be eaten at all)

7.40 Second Helping

7.45 More Pudding

7.46 More 'Pop'

7.47 Community Burping

7.49 Speeches

7.49 & 20 seconds End of Speeches

Lucozade with Sugar in it

or

More 'Pop'

The Goodies Awards – Prize Giving

Announcement of Winners by your Master of Ceremonies Mr. Eddie Waring
Followed by explanation of announcements by Richard Baker

THE GOODIES AWARDS
(Three Nominations in each Category)

For Falling Over Better Than We Do

        Nominations: Charlie Chaplin   107th

                     Michael Crawford — 1st

                     Rodney Marsh   2nd

For Being Very Fancy-Able

                                         2nd 3rd 4th 5th 6th 7th 8th

        Nominations: Half the Young Generation   9th 10th 11th 12th

                    1st   Jane Fonda

                       The other Half of the Young Generation

                               Awarded Tim's Prize!

For Making Us Laugh

        Nominations: Tony Blackburn   Disqualified.

                     The Government's Economic Policy

                     Morecambe and Wise   Awarded special

      1ST AGAIN!   prize 3 £5 for a good try.

THE PRIZES
presented by the President of the United States
Mr David Frost   (name not certain at time of printing)

Cabaret Starring: Tommy Cooper, Rod Hull & his Emu, Randy Newman,
                Paul Simon, The Band, Tom & Jerry and Buster Keaton
                (Three hours of recently discovered film comedy masterpieces)

(Des O'Connor & Engelbert Humperdink have kindly agreed not to appear)

Dancing with Pan's People To the music of The Beatles (special farewell performance)

ee Days Later   Never did turn up! —— **The Queen**

Dear Tim and Bill,

You may have been wondering what I've been doing locked away in my room for the last three days.

Well you're wrong.

I have in fact been designing the new costumes you've been on about. Well, here they are, presented in an easy-to-understand style. All you have to do is cut out the little figures, and stick on the clothes and accessories to get the full impression. As you can see I have striven to preserve, in these designs, the familiar characteristics of us all. Tim, the gay, debonair man about town. Bill, the grotty little gnome. And of course ... Myself, the brilliant, dauntless, awe-inspiring figure we have all come to know and fancy.

Hope you like them,
I await your comments with interest.

Yours,

Graeme

Graeme.

COMMENTS:............................REJECTED.......... Tim
.... Bill
....
....

EAR·MUFFS

SOU-WESTER

IN CASE OF RAIN.

GRAEME

CAPE

IMPRESSIVE SHIRT.

PENCIL

BELT.

BOY-SCOUT DIARY

TIGHTS

WELLIES

PIPE

WRIST - RADIO

COSY MITTENS

MINIATURE CAMERA. (ACTUAL SIZE)

MATCHES

SLIPPERS

JET-THRUST BACK-PACK

ASBESTOS Y-FRONTS

FIRE-EXTINGUISHER

POWDER PUFF

WIG

EYELASHES

VERY VERY SILLY HAT

TIM

O.B.E.

SHOULDER-PADS

SUIT

IN CASE OF SUN

SENSIBLE SHOES

CORSET

BULLET-PROOF HANKIE

PORTABLE GRAMOPHONE FOR 'LAND OF HOPE & GLORY'

HAT

AFTER-SHAVE

BOXING GLOVES

STICKING PLASTER

DISGUISE

KNUCKLE-DUSTERS

SACK

MICROPHONE

AMPLIFIER

SCISSORS

IN CASE OF DEEP SNOW

TASTEFUL TROUSERS

BOVVER PLIMSOLLS

COMFY PULLOVER

BILL

OLD SCHOOL TIE

Wasn't Mister Tim
a lovely little lad?!
What a waste

KLEENO SMALLS LAUNDRY LIMITED

CLIENT ..... *The Goodies* ....

ITEM	NO.	CHECK	£	p
Dirty Vests	3	✓		·60
Pants	3 prs	✓		·60
Hankies	3	✓	15	·05
Shirts	2	✓		·75
Goodies T-shirt	1	✓		·75
Leopard-skin body stocking + hat	none	✗	12	·43
Brown trousers (Tim's)	1 pr	✓	1	·00
Clean Vests	6 doz	✓		·60
Eggs	1 doz	✓	2	·00
6 legged pantomime dromedary skin	15	✗ ✓		·02
Funny clothes - various (Bill's)	1	✓	74	·04
Tights	1 pr	✓		·12
Hot air balloon - (stained)	1	✓		·12
Bra	1	?		·12
Aprons	317	✓	317	·00
Y-Front Hovercraft (small)	1	✓		·50
more Aprons	2	✗	2	·00
Suede safari boots	½ pr	✓		·00
Sausage, bacon, beans, chips + egg (sunny side up)	twice		1	·20

PAID
15 MAR 1974

(+ VAT)   £28,431 - 73

No Liability accepted for Belts, Buckles, Buttons, String, Suspenders or Zips

And see what happens when they get too big for their boots. Pop stars indeed! E.T. (mrs)

GOODIES' TOP SECRET FILE

Title THE RISE AND FALL, (and rise) OF THE GOODIES FEB 1st – FEB 12th 1974

THE GOODIES
SING SONGS FROM
THE GOODIES

DECCA

Melody Maker

GOODIES SPLIT

blues", with tasty guitar Francis of apton?) – in iness" (Bill ne of THE ues lyrics

n damn

soul. ay night

and Roll."

it like it is! an amazing at explodes gins" with nes Brown of; whilst !" is pure "Wolsey" doing a nd all, I

hours; ! The ellent

The savage ups and downs of the pop rat-race have claimed three more victims. It was revealed today that the apparently oh-so-successful-would-be-chart-busters — THE GOODIES - have, in fact decided to break up. BILL ODDIE, musical spokesman for the group, said: "We feel that commercial demands are incompatible with our artistic integrity". Tim Brooke-Taylor elaborated on the statement: "We're skint!" he said. When asked "why?", he suggested "Probably it's because we're such rotten singers". He then burst into tears. Rumours that Graeme Garden is going to go solo were described by the others as ****ing ridiculous.

THE GOODIES

No Fixed Abode, Nr. Cricklewood, London

THIS MINUTE BOOK BELONGS TO:

THE GOODIES

Minutes of a Special Emergency Meeting

A special emergency committee meeting was held outside the
Cricklewood Labour Exchange at IO.I5 am on Monday I6th June.
Tim Brooke-Taylor was in the chair, Graeme Garden was on the
pavement, and Bill Oddie was grovelling in a nearby dustbin.
The main item under discussion was the grave economic crisis
brought about by the recently reported bankruptcy of the Goodies
Pop Group. The treasurer was asked to present his financial
report which is here attached.

He the there was an o~~ld~~ .... obblers
we stung on th .... ubbish
eas hu .... elf
How it ~~Chelsea~~ .... l in
Tim Se ~~lost 3-2~~ .... old
fat el .... lory

BM who ri .... up
trash a .... it
_ll_ -r .... and
we a ....!

In r .... ere.

Dear ....
toda .... st
two .... n't
had ....

On the .... as closer to you,
felt the .... intensity than
earlier .... in the Grunewald.

           chairman then tabled the motion
The ~~committee has therefore decided~~ that we should sign on
with a big powerful agent/manager and have another go.

Motion carried by unanimously with two ~~abstens~~

                              ~~abstain~~

                    not voting

                    T B T

Handwritten attachment (cigarette packet & note):

Treasurer's Financial report — .   16ᵀ June.

GOODIES ACCOUNTS

IN   Records sold -   30,000
      Record company's share - £50,000
        ∴ our share   4·17½p

OUT
      Cost of musicians   £2,100·00
      Cost of musicians' tea   £ 600·12
      Bribery to Disc Jockies (call-girls etc) 3000·09
      Hire of studio's   720·07½
      Cost of records bought to make sure
      it got in the charts -   50,000 4·17½
      Drinks to press -   540·62
              TOTAL £56964·48
BALANCE OWING -   4·17½
  x Graeme £56960·30½p

20 GUT ROTTERS COKE-TIPPED

WARNING by H.M. Government
READING CAN DAMAGE
YOUR HEALTH

Izzy Bent Management Limited
Pop Agent
(Affiliated to The the Low Grade Organisation)

Dear Boys already,
How pleased I was to get your letter oyvay! LOVE your singing! (MUST hear you sometime) Sure, I'd be delighted to ~~bleed you dry~~ represent you. You wanna be stars? No bother, my sons! No sooner said than fiddled. Please sign & return enclosed contract already (enclosing blank cheque) and we'll fix up a meeting.

Love Izzy

Rookem, Screwem and Scarper, (Solicitors), Queer Street, London W2.

Illegal yet binding contract

1. The said ...Goodies... shall be the exclusive property of the said ...Izzy Bent... for a period of five hundred years or life (whichever is the longer)

2. All earnings of the ...Goodies... shall be divided in the proportion of ...50/50...

3. The said ...Izzy Bent... reserves the right to terminate this contract and nip off to ...the Bahamas... He must, however, give due and fair warning of this intention.

Signed: (for Izzy Bent) ...Izzy Bent...
(for the Goodies) ...Graeme Garden Bill Oddie Tim Brooke-Taylor...

Notes

1. The Goodies herein taken to mean T. Brooke-Taylor, G. Garden & B. Oddie or anyone with similar names; their friends, family, children of the next ten generations, dogs, stick insects etc. etc. ....

2. ...50/50... ie. 50p. to The Goodies and £50 to Izzy Bent

3. "Due and fair warning" shall mean 3–5 seconds

The small print

BUCKINGHAM PALACE, LONDON SW1, ENGLAND

Dear Boys already

Thanks for the cheque.
Sorry - can't make meeting just now - am
being knighted. Never mind, take my advice -
get yourself a number one hit record - & you
cant go wrong.

Good luck

Issy.

P.S. How about calling yourselves 'The Goodies' -
Nice one eh? - Dont forget - try to
appeal to the young folk - they've
more gullible.

(please send consultation fee by return)

y. X Issy

UNDER5

The *first* fab-mag for "baby-boppers"

JULY 1974

NAPPY CONTROL
on that very first date

OVER THE HILL?
Interview with Little Jimmy Osmond

IS MUMMY'S MILK FATTENING?
How to keep slim during that difficult first year

THE GRAND OLD MAN OF POP
onny talks to Under5

THE DISCO-NURSERY
fab new idea

THE GOODIES
xclusive

LUS-Pics-fashion-beauty-stories-letters

are you a GROOVY BABY?

UNDER 5 CONTENTS

This month's editor

Meet UNDER 5's playmate of the month

Acknowledgments

Art direction: Anthony Cohen

Designed by: Denis Hawkins, Rod & Kira Josey, Philip Bryden, Arnaldo Putzo, Kieran Stevens, David Ross, John Leach, Miguel Lopez Parras, Vicky Franklin, Martin Andrews and Prince Andrew.

Photography by: Geoff Goode, BBC Radio Times, Lynn News & Advertiser, Mary Evans Picture Library, International Photo Press, Evans Jones, M. Delanoe, Camera Press.

With special thanks to: Tom & Heloise Brooke, Linda and Alice, Danny, and Mrs Reader.

Goodies!
baddies more like

by Annabelle Twee

THE GOODIES could easily be the new rave on the baby-bopper scene this year. After rumours that they were splitting up, these veritable Chelsea Pensioners of Pop have reformed. Goody, goody! say I (*You* would; Ed.) Too old? "Not on your life" says slightly hunchbacked Tim Brooke Taylor, leaping from his bathchair. "How about Gary Glitter?" (How *about* him; Ed.) "He's sixty if he's a day, and I happen to know that's not his own hair". "Yes, I know that too" adds Bill Oddie, "We both get mowed at the same gardener". "The point is" (Graeme Garden speaking) "we are going to give the kiddiwinkies what they *really* want". "And that means lots of violence, kinky

clothes and naughty lyrics" says Bill. "And you should see our new act! We may be called the Goodies, but on stage we're anything but". And it's true . . . I've seen them and Wow! They have this great bit where they all come on as babies and chop up Alice Cooper; then Bill does some AMAZING things with a feeding bottle! And then . . . well, don't believe what you read – go and see for yourself! The Goodies are appearing at the One o'clock Club, Primrose Hill Kindergarten on Monday, and they have a guest spot on the "Woodentops" on Thurs. But . . . and how about *this?* . . . they've been BANNED from TOP OF THE POPS! Oh, AND they are working on a fab new rock stage show; "PIOUS XIV – SUPER POPE" . . . look out for *that*.!

Baby talk

▬BABY BUNTING▬

Outrage stateside! LITTLE JIMMY OSMOND has upset millions of his fans by admitting that he is really 53 years old, a midget, and the FATHER of the so called brothers! . . . but GOOD NEWS for OSMONDS fans . . . from the Maternity Ward where a new OSMOND is expected any day now. The newcomer is set for College Dates as soon as he or she is weened, and he should make a British Tour next year, heading a bill that will include SLY STONE, DUKE ELLINGTON, YEHUDI MENUHIN, MARIA CALLAS, AND THE HALLE ORK . . . some show!
Grave news (ho ho) from NEW YORK, FRANK SINATRA died last week. He starts his fifteenth farewell tour in July . . .

TONY BLACKBURN has just entered Hospital for a head transplant. The donor is believed to be a SCOTS PINE;
Group news; EMERSON LAKE AND PALMER, following their recent split reformed to become LAKE PALMER AND EMERSON: they then split again but got together as PALMER EMERSON AND LAKE. Rumour hath it that there's still trouble . . . expect them to re-appear as LEMERPAL AKER AND SON . . . LULU has split up . . . Round the Clubs: PETER NOONE is recovering from a nasty ordeal. Seems someone mistook him for a VENTRILOQUISTS DOLL and locked him in a suitcase for three weeks. On second thoughts, perhaps it was NO MISTAKE! Byeeeeeee!

BEFORE **AFTER**

NOBODY LOVES A BALD BABY!

ALWAYS "IT"?
DO YOU NEVER GET CAUGHT?
ALL *YOU* NEED IS *HAIR*.
So get a "Bowie" Baby Wig.
Available in Blonde, Brunette, Strawberry & Green.
Different styles available . . .

DINKY DENTS

FED UP WAITING FOR THAT FIRST TOOTH?

Give nature a nudge!
Get a set of DINKY DENTS
REAL TEETH
(collected from the skulls of dead monkies)
"DONNY" phosphorescent paint – extra! Now!

CANVI-NAPS

MADE FROM 100% WATERPROOF RUBBERISED CANVAS*
*As used by Deep Sea Divers & Billy Smarts Circus.

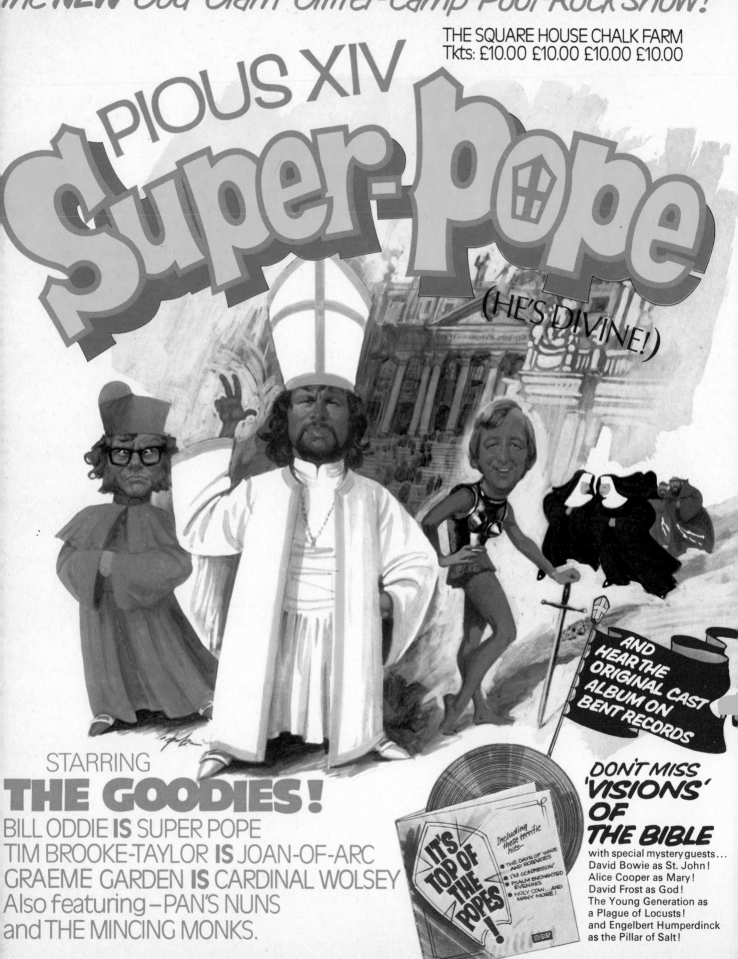

JANUARY 20 1974   No 7858   Price 10p

THE SUNDAY TIMES

Pious XIV, Superpope—a new musical

This tawdry little show (written and performed by Tim Brooke Taylor, Graeme Garden and Bill Oddie) gave me very little pleasure indeed. I found the acting embarrassing, the tunes forgettable and the dancing tedious. When one considers the basic subject matter, one can only lament an opportunity totally squandered. In vain I looked for spiritual dignity, historical veracity or a quick flash of pubic hair. At the final curtain I was so outraged that I was moved to sigh; and I fell off my surgical support and damaged my hearing aid, which only then had been mercifully switched off throughout. The audience loved it; and they loved the show too. No doubt it will run for years . . .

British Le

ALBUM REVIEW
SUPER-POPE — SUPER TRIP

Yeah, man, this is some heavy **** For a long time now these dudes have been threatening to get their **** together. Well, wait no more amigos, man, this is IT. What a mind blower! *****! It doesn't take a pretentious spaced-out head like me to spot the clue in the title. Super POPE . . . Dig the rhyme? POPE — DOPE . . . Right? THAT'S where it's at . . . and how! Whoooosh! ******* Far out, too much . . . like ****** . . . NICE . . . yeah . . . al RIGHT. . . . hmmmmmm . . . zzzzzzzzz(SNORE)

. . . threatening to get

Melody Maker
FEBRUARY 9, 1974   9p weekly   USA 50 cents

#	(last)	Title
1	(1)	**PIOUS XIV – SUPER-POPE (ORIGINAL CAST)** . . . . . . The Goodies, Bent
2	(4)	**20 ORIGINAL HITS** The Session Singers, K Tel
3	(2)	**A TRIBUTE TO ELDRIDGE CLEAVER** The Black and White Minstrels, Bootleg
4	(7)	**MOTOWN CHARTBUSTERS VOL 237** Various Unknowns, Motown
5	(11)	****TO THE LOT OF YOU** John Lennon, Apple
6	(3)	**SLEEPALONGAMAX VOL 94** Max Bygones, Pye
7	(–)	**CLIFF'S DIRTY SONG BOOK** Cliff Richard, Rhubarb Tart
8	(6)	**THE LAST TRAM TO WIGAN** BBC Sound Effects Dept., BBC
9	(5)	**RIP YOUR KNICKERS OFF – I'M EVIL** The Osmonds, MGM
10	(–)	**THE YING TONG SONG ETC** Prince Charles, OBE

ALBUM OF THE MONTH

PIOUS XIV SUPER POPE
(Original Cast)
Bent. Quintuple album

This five record package represents nearly everything that is good about British Rock Music. Certainly, there are some flaws – sides five and nine are identical, and side seven has nothing on it at all – but there's more than enough good music on the other eight sides to keep the average fan happy for several minutes.

And what a range! It's ALL in here; echoes of Joan Baez, The Mothers of Invention, The Beatles, David Cassidy, Des O'Connor, Hendrix, Jimmy Osmond, Gilbert and Sullivan and The New York Dolls – and somehow, it works! Side two opens with a funky little thing sung by Joan of Arc (Tim Brooke Taylor) that sounds for all the world as if Moira Anderson is gigging with Grand Funk Railroad. Believe me, it's a complete gas. Other highlights include "Papal Blues", with some incredibly tasty guitar licks by "St Francis of Assissi" (Eric Clapton?) – in which "His Holiness" (Bill Oddie) gets off some of THE most poignant blues lyrics since Blind Lemon.

"I can bless you, I can damn
  you,
I can consecrate yo' soul.
But when it's Sat'day night
  at the Vat.
I just love to Rock and Roll."

Talk about telling it like it is! "Holy Ghost" is an amazing Moog freak-out that explodes into "Six Wise Virgins" with a bass riff that James Brown would be proud of; whilst "Cardinal's Crunch" is pure Slade — with "Wolsey" (Graeme Garden) doing a Noddy (top hat and all, I bet).

I could go on for hours; and the music does! The recording quality is excellent (remixed in Octophonic, at the thirty-two track studio in the Cistine Chapel, St Peter's, Rome) and the packaging is more than generous. The records come in a presentation gold casket, with forty-seven volumes of Belotti's "History of Catholicism" and a free-give-away original Michelangelo cartoon. Naturally with this kind of quality, it's not cheap, but if you're down to your last £546.17. here's how to spend it. You won't regret it.

Melody Maker
FEBRUARY 2, 1974
9p weekly
USA 50 cents

THE Sun
FORWARD WITH THE PEOPLE
Monday, February 4, 1974

LAND OF POPE AND GLORY

At last! A really good fun evening in the Theatre. And ... wait for it ... it's British! So let's give three hearty cheers!!! One each for the three stars of this all action-dancing-singing-rocking-rave up of a musical. "Wow! If the Vatican's really like this, I'll switch any day", said the Archbishop of Canterbury in the bar at the interval. "And who was there on the stage doing the old knees-up with those pert and pretty Nuns in the finale?

You've guessed it – the old Archbish himself! It certainly brought the colour back to HIS cheeks; and it will to yours. So, go on, go and get an eyeful (and an earful) of the prancing prelate and the rest of the gang; you won't regret it. I was converted – and you'll be too; and I wouldn't mind betting my relics on that!

Welcome to Bri

A POPE-ULAR HIT!

Yes it's all here! Visions of Heaven (and what visions! the most nubile nuns *you've* ever seen), pageants of Purgatory, and the Fires of Hell. And when the temperature goes up, the trousers come down – it's THAT kind of show! Laughs, laughs all the way. The tunes are as infectious as a plague of boils; and the singing would rattle the walls of Jericho. Paradise regained? Blimey mate, I should say so!

Daily Mirror
EUROPE'S BIGGEST DAILY SALE
No. 21,786
Monday, February 4, 1974

Izzy Bent Management Limited
Pop Agent
(Affiliated to The the Low Grade Organisation)

My dear boys already,
I am so happy for you - and me!
Knew you'd make it! What can I say -
except - here's my bill to date (enclosed)
Would appreciate payment by return post -
in used notes. Wouldn't want "anything
to happen to you".
                    Love Izzy

THE GOODIES

Minutes of a <u>Special Emergency Meeting</u>

A special committee meeting was held under the Cricklewood
Park bandstand at 9.45 on 28 July. Bill Oddie was in the
chair, Graeme Garden was in the Gents, and Tim Brooke-Taylor
was in tears. The treasurer was called upon to present his
financial report, which is here reproduced.

<u>INCOME</u>

1½ million copies of "Super Pope" Album, personal appearances, etc.	£2,500,568.17p
Less Agents %	£1,900,234.02p
	£ 56,960.30½p
Money owing to previous debtors on record account	£ 56,960.30½p
Total due to <u>US</u>	£0,000,000.00p

FILE CLOSED

GOODIES SPLIT!

The wicked rat race of Rock and Roll claims three more victims. Despite selling one and a half million records in three weeks, The GOODIES have decided to split up. Bill Oddie, Musical Spokesman for the group, said: "The pressures of being a Super Group were just too heavy for us. Somehow the music was suffering. We've decided to cool it and just do our own thing for a while." Graeme Garden added: "This business is full of people who are "not very nice". I won't mention any names otherwise the "Boys" will be round to see us." Tim Brooke Taylor has started crying again . . .

panicles of red berries if you let it, is usu
grown in gardens in its wonderful golden,
leaved form *plumosa aurea*. One's object, '
this shrub, is to obtain the handsomest pos
display of foliage, and to this end re
pruning back of young wood should be p
sed in the dormant season. I have no

now. In fact I've got thre
like the one I was first
duced to; I've got a simil
but with a head that ligh
that one seems to turn m
friends on when they're u
– and I've got a big one tha
interchangeable heads. T

STOP PRESS

GOODIES REFORM
THE GOODIES have re-
signed for Decca records.
A new Album will be
released any minute now.
Will they NEVER learn!?

THE QUEEN,
BUCKINGHAM PALACE
~~LONDON~~   ♡→ TIM

away for weekends
~~try~~ SANDRINGHAM
~~Norfolk~~.

No longer this address
try
~~Windsor Castle~~
~~Middlesex~~

on holiday, try "BRITTANIA"
THE PACIFIC OCEAN

by
Buckingham Palace, London

RETURN TO SENDER.

S.W.A.L.K.

THE GOODIES
No Fixed Abode, Nr. Cricklewood, Lon

~~Dear Miss, Mrs Lis Elisa L Elise Eliss Elise~~ Betty Queen ~~MAd~~ Majesty
~~Your majesty~~

Oh Queen,

~~Please can we have three O.B.E.s?~~

Well, here we are in November again and, as we expect you know, it is only fifty seven days to the New Year's Honours' List comes out. ~~Please can we have three O.B.E.s?~~ No doubt you have been thinking who to ~~dish out the gongs to~~ honour, and have a few names in mind already - lucky ~~sods~~ persons. You must be very busy and no doubt you sometimes forget people who really OUGHT to have O.B.E.s ...like what you did last year.
Anyway, just in case you're stuck - may we suggest ourselves?
We think we ought to have O.B.E.s because Tim looks very nice in a sash. (See photo enclosed) Graeme is very clever and Bill will hit us if he's left out.

Yours hopefully,

THE GOODIES

P.S. Can we have them before Christmas so we can hang them on the tree?
P.P.S. If you give one to Des O'Connor, Hughie Green, David Frost or Jimmy Osmond, we'll send ours back.
P.P.P.S. If Charles fancies a part in one of our shows we will gladly give him an audition.

P.P.P.P.S. Why dont you ever do a fullslength picture on the stamps — I bet you've got smashing legs — B.71.

P.P.P.P.P.S. I shall be behind the pelican's feeding hut in St. James' Park on Sat. at 5.0'clock — hint hint
Tim X.

The Goodies — Tax Relief in year ended April 1973~~4~~ ³ ²   Hello!

£ / p

	£	p
Gross Income:	28,431	73
Tax Due on this amount:	29,431	73
Claims for Tax Relief:	1,894³	73
Support of a dependant (Tim)	103	94
" " " (Graeme)	103	94
" " " (Bill)	½ cup of rice (value 103-94)	
Employment of Mrs. E. Tole (cleaner)	13,437	08 (+ blackmail)
Clothes (Protective)	7,930	43
Hire of one six-legged Dromedary Skin	155	00
Japanese lunch	10,000,071	31 (YEN)
Doctor's fees	59	04 (IRISH YEN)
Accountant's fees for converting yen to sterling	5,000	00 (YEN)
More accountant's fees	28,431	73
Rental of ½ hundredweight of fungus (assorted)		01
Professional expenses	29,431	73

Total owed by Dept. of Inland Revenue to The Goodies: 23,431·73

Plus VAT 10% £ **29,431-73** p

Signed:

Lois Comm:

D. Nominator

TOTAL: £ ~~76,984~~ 00 p.

76,953-00 p.

well!

The Goodies — Tax year ended April 1973/4

	£ Pounds Shillings Pence	£

INCOME

194.00
76.83½
2,5193½

From : H.M. Government for hushing up Hovercraft scandal	50,000	00½
" : T.W. Stegendorf for supplying a hat	32	03
" : I.C.I. for discovering of synthetic petrol		NONE
" : Archbishop of Canterbury (for services rendered)		25
" : Mummy on Tim's birthday	76	83½
" : "Loony" Jack Stremblie for laying lino	194,000	00
" : Oxfam		½ cup of rice (value 1·24p)
" : Ex-King Zog of Albania		2 only
" : "A friend" for fixing the election Total :-	$ 300	00

32.03
+ NONE
39.08

527·09.
24½
143·
12·
8·
09

28,489 54½
29,730 29,434

EXPENDITURE

money money	Rent, rates, light, heating, food.		8	37
money	Telephone		3,017	24¼
money	Hire of 6-legged Dromedary Skin		55	00
	Magnifying glass and curly pipe	✓ 6/10 Fair.	21	53
	Clothes (Protective)		7,930	42
money money	Haircuts			NONE
money MONEY	Legal Fees			73
MONEY			3,521	349

MONEY!

| Fees for professional services to Lois Comm, and D. Nominator: ➡ | 28,431 | 73 |

Buy Mercedes tomorrow

Signed: Tim Brooke-Taylor

G.G. / Oddie

Received with thanks Lois Comm.

| TOTAL OWING :- | 28,431 | 73 p |

signed
Lois Comm.

HOW TO BE
A Bird-Watcher

A SHORT BOOK BY Bill Oddie

Chapter 1
Why watch birds?

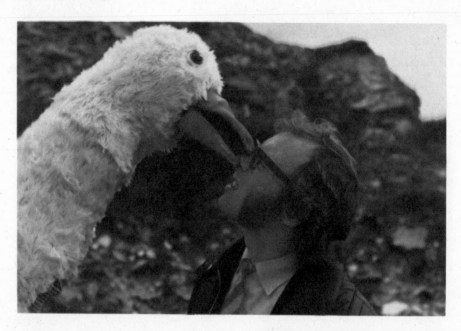

Why *not?* I resent this question. There's nothing *weird* about me, you know – I'm not a crank or something. I just happen to like watching birds, and that's THAT. And I don't want any of your silly remarks like "BIRD watcher oh yes? Eh Eh?" or "I'm a bit of a BIRD watcher too – TWO LEGGED variety . . . know what I mean?" Yes, ho ho, very funny. Well show me a bird that *hasn't* got two legs (unless of course you've chopped one of them off) I just happen to LIKE watching birds – do you MIND? Well, it's better than watching Yeti's or stones (which are quite boring and can't sing) or indeed Elephants (Cos Elephants can't fly so well). And a good thing too you say, I expect. Couldn't resist it could you? Well, that's a boring old joke. Almost as boring and old as "BIRD watcher eh eh?" So PACK IT IN and STOP GETTING AT ME. Or I shall CRY.

*A "Wombat" has in fact four legs; but most scientists would say a wombat is not a bird – and how right they would be.

Chapter 2
What do I need to watch birds with?

a) Eyes
b) A GOOD pair of binoculars. Or, If you're poor, a BAD pair of binoculars. These should be easy to handle, and NOT TOO HEAVY; otherwise, when you put them round your neck, you'll fall over.

Chapter 3
What should I wear to watch birds in?

When you are poking round the countryside, peering in bushes through your binoculars, NEVER wear bright conspicuous clothes – you'll only draw attention to yourself and people will wonder what on earth you are doing. ALWAYS wear a dirty green floppy hat, a dirty green floppy anorak and dirty green floppy socks. I would also recommend a pair of waterproof pants – in case you see a rare bird and get over-excited. (Think about it . . .)

At all times it is essential that the birds do not see YOU. If they do, they will fall about laughing. You will then get upset.

It is therefore most important to find something in which you can completely secrete yourself when watching birds. Which brings us to HIDES.

Chapter 4
What is a hide?

Something in which you can completely secrete yourself when watching birds.

Chapter 5
How can I completely secrete myself when watching birds?

Get a HIDE, Dummy! Honestly! Questions questions! HERE are some different kinds of HIDES.

A tree hide

Disadvantages

It is impossible to reach your eyes with your binoculars when your arms are stuck down a hollow branch.

BEWARE OF Beavers, Woodpeckers, Dogs. (Also, in spring, when the sap is rising, beware of other trees).

Wildfowlers Decoy

This should be very effective for getting really close to water birds. (I have not actually tried it myself. If anyone does have a go, please write and tell me if there are any disadvantages.)

A Canvas Hide

Disadvantages

When bird-watching on building-sites, this hide is easily mistaken for a temporary toilet.

Beware of Irish labourers after lunchbreak.

'Natural' Disguise

Disadvantages

Fools nobody! Least of all a bird. But, just in case, don't try it in the mating season.

Waterproof Wellies.

Chapter 6
Where can I watch birds?

a) The Natural History Museum*
b) Trafalgar Square**
c) The Snowdon Aviary (London Zoo)***
d) Wild birds – not so easy. BUT . . . if you REALLY want to see lots and lots of really beautiful wild birds, find out where the government are going to build the next Airport or Power Station and go there – QUICKLY !

*Most of the birds here are, in fact, dead – but this makes it easier to watch them. Anyway, if you kick the glass case (when the attendant isn't looking) they do move . . . a bit . . . and you can PRETEND they are alive.

**Don't look up.

***Usually closed for repair. The birds do a lot of damage trying to get out of this big nasty cage.

Chapter 7
What do I do when I see a bird?

Blimey, you want to be told everything don't you? It's up to you what you do. Some people jump up and down, others roll on the floor giggling, others turn round and run away. You can stand on your head and sing Ave Maria for all I care.

If you really HAVE to be told . . . you should carry a note book and take detailed and accurate notes on where you saw the bird, when, the weather conditions, what it looked like etc etc. Here, for an example, is a typical page from my Bird Note Book.

Chapter 8
A typical page from my note book

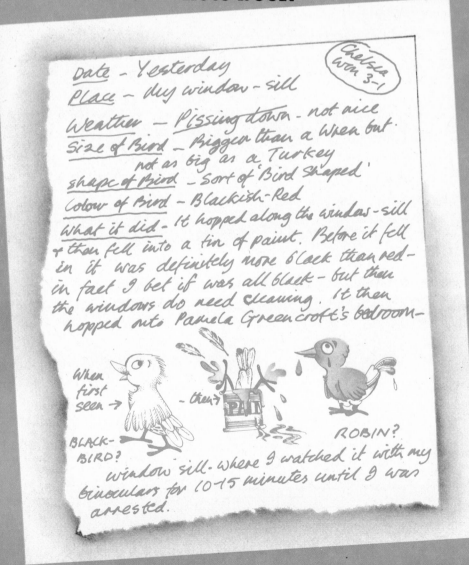

Date – Yesterday
Place – my window-sill
Weather – Pissing down - not nice
Size of Bird – Bigger than a Wren but not as big as a Turkey
shape of Bird – Sort of 'Bird Shaped'
Colour of Bird – Blackish-Red
What it did – It hopped along the window-sill + then fell into a tin of paint. Before it fell in it was definitely more black than red – in fact I bet it was all black – but then the windows do need cleaning. It then hopped onto Pamela Greencroft's bedroom-

Chelsea won 3-1

When first seen →
BLACK-BIRD?

- then →
PAINT

ROBIN?

window sill - where I watched it with my binoculars for 10-15 minutes until I was arrested.

Chapter 9
An Introduction to bird identification

A Duck *

A Lovable little Blue Tit **

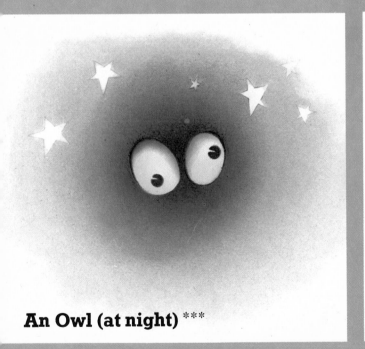

An Owl (at night) ***

A Sainsbury's Chicken ****

*Delicious – in bread sauce with an orange stuffed up its parson's nose.

** Not a full meal.

***If you enjoy the flavour of voles and shrews, this is most appetising. N.B. Make sure it is an owl and not a West Indian (not so tasty).

****Flightless.

THE OBSERVERS BOOK OF BIRD WATCHERS

OF

BIRD WATCHERS

Spot 'Em a Mile Off:

'Retired Colonel'   'Frustrated Spinster'   'Loony'

They're all in here

Coming Soon in the Same Series
The Observers book of:
Concorde
Terrapins
Brian Clough
Observers

Japanese Binoculars

Ideal for spies, voyeurs and bird watcher (eh eh?)

This amazing precision instrument – tiny, yet perfect in every detail – except one (we won't spoil the fun by telling you which one). See the world like you've never seen it before – totally distorted. The Birds immediately come 8 times closer – to have a look at your squitty little binoculars!

FANTASTIC VALUE – Only 50p a pair (plus £50 VAT, £75.75 Postage and Packing and compulsory plastic carrying case £105.21).

AVAILABLE ON 3 MINUTES APPROVAL
Just send cash for full amount and you can try these magnificent binoculars in your own home for 3 Minutes. If you are not satisfied just send them back and we won't be in the least bit hurt (as long as we can keep the money).

ORDER NOW – From The Back of a Lorry (Optics), Surrey Docks, London.

Remember our Feathered Friends
Wild Bird Food

"Glide" – Fruit, nuts and seeds. Ideal for blue tits, sparrows and finches. 50p per lb
"Gobble" – Blue-tits, sparrows and finches. Ideal for owls and hawks. £1.25 per lb.
"Yeuch" – Gravel and sawdust. Birds won't touch it – very cheap £0.1p per ton.
"Scrummy" – Six festering buffalos – deep frozen (maggots extra). Vultures love them! £6.25.
"Alarm Clocks" – In packets of 12. Irresistible to Ostriches. £12.70.
"Steak and Chips" – with courgettes, champignons, pommes frittes, zabaglione, coffee and cheese. Choice of wine (4 persons). £20.16 + V.A.T.

Attract the BIRDS to YOUR garden.

NEST BOXES
Small size – suitable for Blue Tits etc £1.50 Large Size – suitable for Vultures, Ostriches or 12 Pakistanis £25.00

All our products available at 60% above the normal price to anyone daft enough to pay.

BIRD TABLES
"Natural". Stands on the ground. Indistinguishable from a piece of wood £2.50

"TRENDY"
£17.00
Aluminium with glass top

BIRD CHAIRS
Birds are not in fact in the habit of sitting on chairs – but you will enjoy hours of merry laughter watching them try!

AND MORE FUN!
TIT FEEDER
See the little tits trying to get at their food, swinging up side down for hours, till the blood rushes to their heads and they fall off £3.50

BIRD CUSHION
For Soft landing when the little tits fall off £5.15

HEATED BIRD BATH.
This bath will hold up to 17 greenfinches at a time. It is made of white or pink porcelain, and comes with a non-slip rubber bath mat and two cakes of soap (loofahs extra).
In cold weather the thermostat automatically switches on the gas flame beneath – thus heating the bath water!
A Real Joy for the birds when they are cold and hungry.
(Or if you are cold and hungry – set the thermostat to 'boiling' and within seconds – hey presto! – nourshing Greenfinch Soup)

Available from... **Tweeti Products** "The Nest" Tweeville, Bucks.

Rescued from fire
9 Nov '73 E.T. (mrs)

GOODIES'
TOP SECRET FILE

Title. *THE CASE OF "THE ROYAL COMMAND"*

EVER SO
EVER SO
SECRET

IF YOU SEE THIS FILE
★ DESTROY IT ★
IF YOU SEE THIS FILE

ON SECOND THOUGHTS
YOU NEVER SAW IT~

This must be burned.

BUCKINGHAM PALACE, LONDON SW1, ENGLAND

Dear Goodies

I hope you do not mind me writing to you, but I am fed up, and I think you may be able to help. It's a long story but, well, here goes.

As you probably know, next Saturday is this year's Royal Variety Show (yawn yawn). Mum and Dad said I have got to go with them, but I said, I don't want to. I said, I don't like sitting through three hours of boring jugglers, and rotten Spanish ventriloquists and Des O'Connor and poncy posh ballet dancers. I mean, I <u>know</u> Mum and Dad <u>like</u> having jokes made about them and being bowed to and all that, 'cos it makes them feel wanted - but, well, all that 'variety' stuff may be OK for old folks (like <u>them</u>, tee hee) but it's not my scene. I asked Mum why she couldn't get The Slade or Sweet or Monty Python (rude bits and all!!). She said "Wash your mouth out!" and anyway none of them are signed to Lew Grade so they'd <u>never</u> be in it. So we had one heck of a stinking row. Well, to cut a long story short, they've said if I don't want to go, I needn't, but I shall jolly well be locked up in my room on Saturday night, <u>and</u> I've got to write out 100 times 'Max Bygraves is not a boring old fart'. <u>And</u> what's more they've cut my pocket money down to £2000 a week, <u>and</u> Dad says he's not going to buy me the Goons LP for Christmas after all.

So anyway - I've decided I shall jolly well have my Own Royal Variety Show - in My room (with 'tuck and pop!') Charles told me to write to the Goons but they can't come (actually Peter Sellers wanted too much money, Spike Milligan is away defending a daisy, and Harry Secombe is in the real Royal Variety Show - cheek! singing flippin' Welsh operas though, I bet, and not doing silly voices) and, well, Monty Python are a bit <u>past it</u> now aren't they? So I thought I'd ask you to come and do it.

Any chance?

Yours hopefully

Andrew

Andrew (Prince)

THE GOODIES

No Fixed Abode, Nr. Cricklewood, London

Wednesday 14th inst.

Dear Sir or Prince,

Thank you for your kind enquiry of the 12th inst.
We think we know the kind of thing that you have in mind and are pleased
to enclose our estimate for the proposed "entertainment".

Trusting that you will find our terms acceptable.

Yours,

The Goodies

THE GOODIES

Alternative Royal Variety Performance

Estimate

Time: 2 hours approximately

To hiring performers: Tim Brooke Taylor at £25 per hour............. £50
Graeme Garden at £25 per hour................. £50
Bill Oddie at 50p per hour.................... £01
To writing basic script...................................... £10
To hire of trandem ....
One falling over routine; 3 mins. at £6 per min. £05
Funny business on bike; 2 mins. at £10 per min. ....: £18
Bill's song; 3 mins. at £0.05 per min. £20
To hiring custard pies, red noses, whoopee cushions, ... £00.15
revolving bow ties, six legged pantomime dromedary skin, etc. £75

Total.................... £229.15
plus V.A.T.

10% deposit acceptable on acceptance of Estimate

BUCKINGHAM PALACE, LONDON SW1, ENGLAND

Thursday 15th inst.

Dear Goodies

Thanks for your estimate - a bit steep, but - oh well - look, I'm
a bit short of the 'ready' right now - will you accept payment in
marbles, dead mice, OBE's, Crown Jewels, etc? Anticipating your
agreement I enclose a deposit of an orb and sceptre, a sash of the
Order of the Garter (slightly used), and a dead mouse.

See you 8.00 clock? Saturday

Yours

Andrew

PS - Mum and Dad will be livid if they find out what I'm up to.
Please try and slip in without anyone noticing. I enclose a plan
of the Palace.

How To Break Into Buckingham Palace

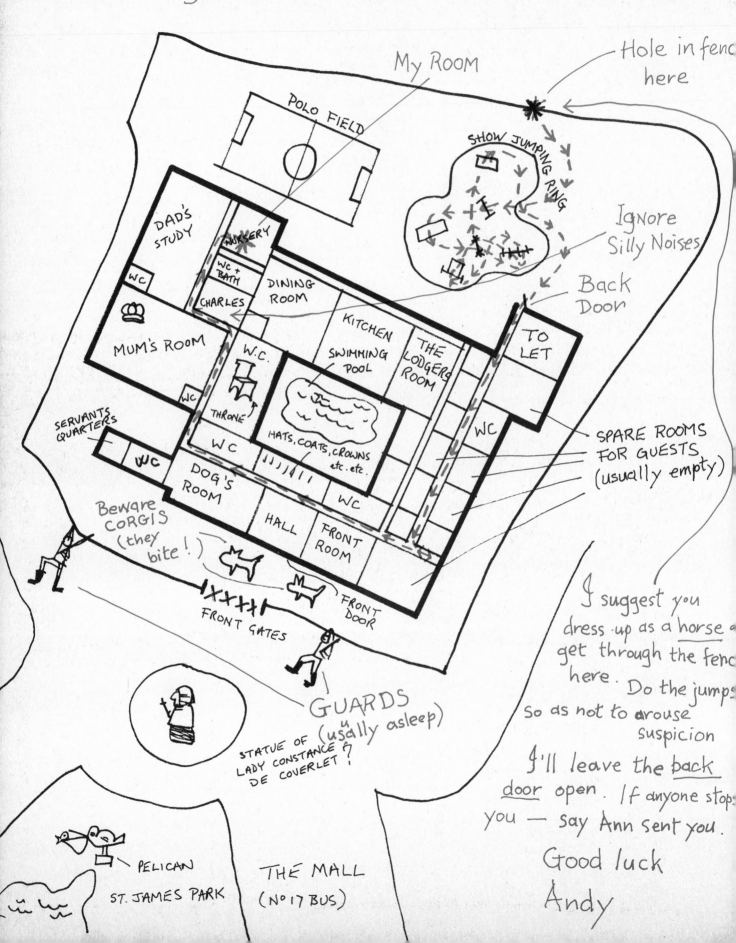

ROYAL [INST]RUCTIONS

...I have managed to prune or spray fruit trees, mend the glass of one of the green-houses, take down the dead tendrils of two very tall clematis plants or carry in pine cones to use as kindling. These things have to be done sooner or later. They can be put off, unlike a publisher's deadline, and so I feel virtuous when I have done what I might have left until tomorrow. In the week just ended... ...suppose I should be content my work at... ...all turn, a pair of comedian ALL at once the resident field-hen food stacked on the bench. potting shed discovered the been there for several weeks without mice were about, but yesterday whe at things on the bench I saw the av layer pellets. I decided to get in for th bins up in the old...

re were unprecedented scenes at Royal Variety Show last night en the Royal Party walked out at f time, after giving the Black and ite Minstrels the slow hand clap.

just wasn't Her ty's night! For, re-ng home earlier than ted, she was struck in ce by a custard pie. It believed to have been n by one of her sons prefers to remain ymous) who was, he MS, defending himself an onslaught of similar directed at him by ee unknown men". This y was later corroborated e Prince's father, who indeed catch sight of ee men" climbing over alace railings. A slight-orn six legged panto-e dromedary skin was r found hanging from of the spikes. ter reports, from two

Horseguards and a corgi, suggested that the three men ran off down the Mall carrying a sack. The sack is believed to contain twenty-five O.B.E.s, a small throne and most of the Crown Jewels.

The Prince was visibly affected by the incident and has only just stopped laugh-ing. He is at present re-covering on the Royal Yacht somewhere in the South Pacific and is un-available for comment.

Police are anxious to establish the identity of the "three men". If caught, they could be charged with "High Treason"; if found guilty they will either be beheaded or incur a £5 fine.

NEW SCOTLAND YARD

FROM: SUPERINTENDANT BENT(TREASON)   TO: FOTO FIT DEPT....
PLEASE CONSTRUCT FOTO FIT PICTURES OF THE 'THREE MEN', FROM THE
FOLLOWING EYE WITNESS DESCRIPTIONS.

SERGEANT DOBBIN (HORSE GUARD)

'THERE WAS THIS TALL UN WIV FUZZY BITS ON HIS FACE....
AND ENORMOUS GLASSES. I THINK HE HAD A CAT ON HIS HEAD.
THE MIDDLE SIZED ONE HAD LONG BLONDE TRESSES AND A TIE,
AND THE LITTLE ONE WAS, AS FAR AS I COULD SEE, COMPLETELY
COVERED IN HAIR.'

TRAMP (NO FIXED ABODE)

'THE FIRST BLOKE WAS PAST ME SO QUICK I ONLY NOTICED
HIS LEFT EAR. THE SECOND ONE HAD BLONDE HAIR STICKING
STRAIGHT UP. AND THE LITTLE ONE WAS BALD..I THINK...BUT
THEN TO BE HONEST I WAS FAST ASLEEP ON THE PARK BENCH SO
HOW SHOULD I KNOW?'

CORGI: STANLEY BALDWIN 3RD (BUCKM PAL.)

'WOOF WOOF GRRRR SNARL SNARL....(KICK) WHIMPER WHIMPER.'

METROPOLITAN POLICE
WANTED
FOR HIGH TREASON
HAVE YOU SEEN
THESE MEN

REWARD: THREE FREE TICKETS TO NEXT YEAR'S ROYAL VARIETY SHOW —OR FIVE POUNDS IN PREMIUM BONDS, IF YOU CAN IDENTIFY THEM

ANY INFORMATION PLEASE TO: SUPERINTENDANT THUG, NEW SCOTLAND YARD

BUCKINGHAM PALACE, LONDON SW1, ENGLAND

Dear Super

The three men are called

THE GOODIES   and I claim my £5*

Yours Edward

* You can stuff the tickets!

Charges to pay

Tariff £

V.A.T. £

Total £

RECEIVED

POST OFFICE

TELEGRAM

Prefix.   Time handed in.

Office of origin and Service Instructions.   Words.

No._____

OFFICE STAMP

By

5 FEB. 74

BENT SCOTLAND YARD

BRITTANIA SOUTH PACIFIC 1700

DEAR SUPER STOP
I DONT KNOW WHO THE THREE MEN ARE STOP AND
HAVE NEVER REPEAT NEVER SEEN THEM BEFORE STOP
EVEN IF I HAVE SEEN THEM BEFORE THEY ARE DEFINITELY
NOT REPEAT NOT THE GOODIES STOP ANYONE WHO SAYS THEY
ARE IS A ROTTEN FIBBER STOP REPEAT STOP =
ANDREW PRINCE STOP + +

or free repetition of doubtful words telephone "TELEGRAMS ENQUIRY"
office of delivery. Other enquiries should be accompanied

all, nobody is going to look at an object of repulsion. Once she

...like to interview, like Salvador Dali and Mick Jagger, and sent it to the Editor of a very famous Fleet Street newspaper with a colour supplement. Unfortunately, poor old Angela hadn't done her homework properly. Yes, her list of famous people included two or three who were already deceased and interred.

Police Baffled

Police are no nearer to establishing the identity of the "three men", after Prince Charles made a dramatic denial today. Scotland Yard have called in The Goodies to help them try and solve the case.

P.C. Bent has announced his retirement. He will now devote two days to writing a book entitled "Great Unsolved Mysteries of 1973" – to be serialized only in **this** paper!

Stop Press

Goodies Find the Jewels

The missing crown jewels and the small throne were today returned to Buckingham Palace after The Goodies stumbled across them in a dustbin outside Buckingham Palace. A spokesman for The Goodies said: "I suppose someone must have thrown them out by mistake."

Cup — 3rd Round
Half-Times
Chelsea 7   Leeds 0
C. Palace v Rochdale
(declared No Contest)
Arsenal   Spurs
(retired hurt)

Racing at Nonbury
3.00 Entrecote Stakes
1. Queen's Stakes
2. Fancy Queen
3. Saucy Fu...

BY APPOINTMENT

PACIFIC OCEAN

a nice tan but a bit sea-sick. Anyway. must close now. Thanks a lot, and remember — MUM'S THE WORD! eh? Yours gratefully A.

The Goodies London.

FILE CLOSED

THE GOODIES
No Fixed Abode, Nr. Cricklewood, London

24th inst.

Dear Sir or Prince,

Nuff said! Our lips are sealed.

Yours,
THE GOODIES

P.S. Hope no one missed the O.B.E.s!!

The Commissioner of Police

Metropolitan Division

London

Nr. Godalming

telephone 999

To:

Ch. Insp. G.W. Bottle,
F Div.,
G/936 - AA7.

Friends in High Places ?!!!

E. J. (Mrs)

My dear ~~Nancy~~, *George*

May I begin by offering you my warmest congratulations on nailing the East Acton Tuesday Sewing Circle and Terrorist Club - as nasty a bunch of villains as ever drew pensions. And of course a heartfelt "well done!" for yet again winning the Lucky Spot Waltz at the Ball. How <u>do</u> you keep it up?

However, I'm afraid I must turn to graver matters. It has regrettably been brought to my notice that there is some concern over the recent behaviour of one of your lads - and it may not surprise you to know I'm speaking of P.C. Bent 362436.

Now we all know the sort of goings on that give us a bad name, but we're men of the world - I'll always turn a blind eye to a little innocent bribery (as long as the price is right) - but you know as well as I do we can't allow a Copper to take the law into his own hands. This Bent lad has apparently started some sort of personal campaign against my old friends the Goodies. (As you will remember, they were very helpful to us in the "Palace" case, since when they have enjoyed Police Protection on the usual terms.) We simply can't have constables carrying on like Wyatt Earp and upsetting the system. Apparently he has got himself mixed up with some woman, and I needn't spell out what that can lead to. (Though in your case, perhaps I do.)

I need hardly remind you that this letter is highly confidential, and rather than trust the usual channels, I am giving it to my new cleaning lady to deliver to you by hand. (Incidentally, she came to me from the Goodies with glowing references, so I know she can be trusted.)

The facts in this 'Bent' case are as follows:

P.C. Bent has recently purchased a curly pipe and violin, and has started looking thoughtful (a bad sign in a copper).

The lad has been taking a lot of time off, but instead of drinking tea, has been spending time in the Criminal Records Office. Looking for something?

Half a brick is missing from stores.

He was seen, only yesterday, in a heavy beard and long black wig, which almost concealed his helmet, entering a shop in the West End run by E.J. Beamont and Co., well known theatrical suppliers of 6-legged pantomime

P.T.O.

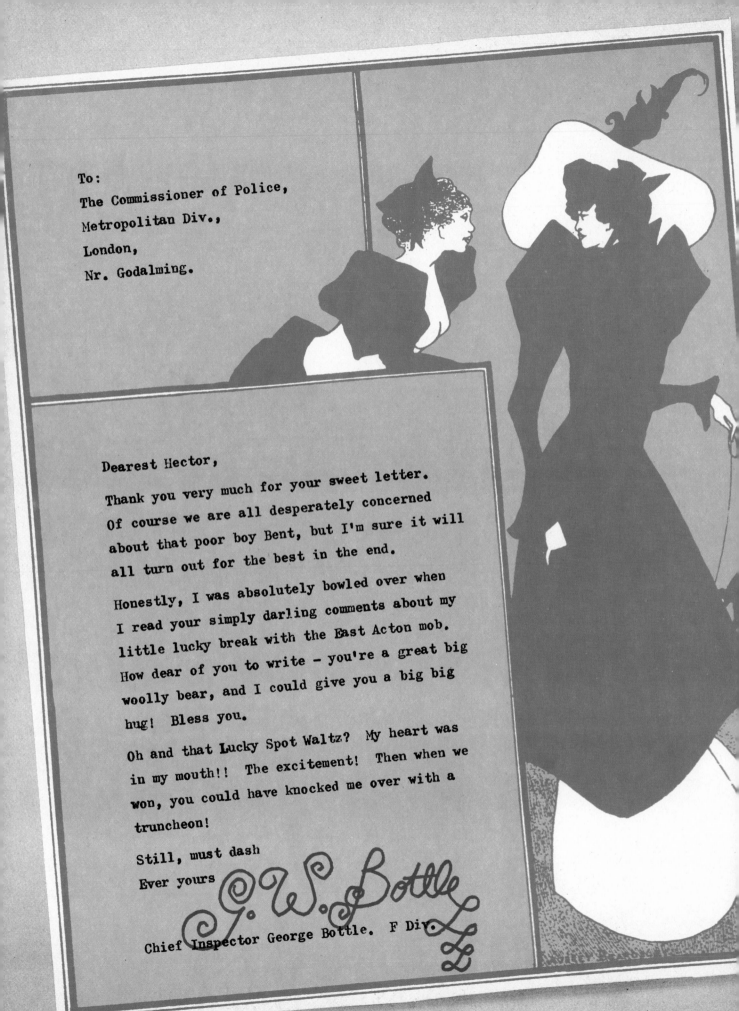

To:
The Commissioner of Police,
Metropolitan Div.,
London,
Nr. Godalming.

Dearest Hector,

Thank you very much for your sweet letter.
Of course we are all desperately concerned
about that poor boy Bent, but I'm sure it will
all turn out for the best in the end.

Honestly, I was absolutely bowled over when
I read your simply darling comments about my
little lucky break with the East Acton mob.
How dear of you to write - you're a great big
woolly bear, and I could give you a big big
hug! Bless you.

Oh and that Lucky Spot Waltz? My heart was
in my mouth!! The excitement! Then when we
won, you could have knocked me over with a
truncheon!

Still, must dash
Ever yours   G. W. Bottle

Chief Inspector George Bottle. F Div.

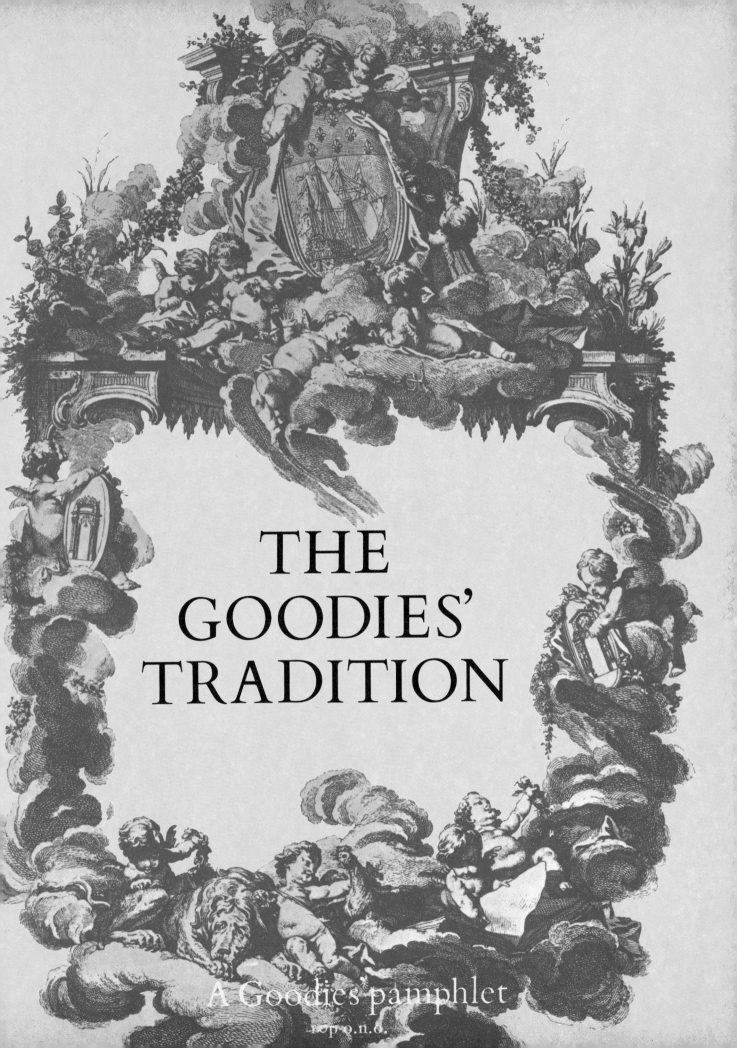

THE GOODIES' TRADITION

A Goodies' pamphlet

The Goodies Tradition

Early cave painting – Lascaux

"Throughout the ages there have always been men prepared to stand up and fight for what is right, proper, and good. Such men as these are *The Goodies*. Their essential spirit, and the spirit of those that came before them, has been captured by the world's greatest artists since the dawn of civilization, and often quite prettily. Anyway I think so. Jolly nice. Alright?"

Sir Kenneth Clark

n Urn (by courtesy of
tish Museum.)

The Bayeux Tapestry (detail)

hIC EST TRANDEM   ET

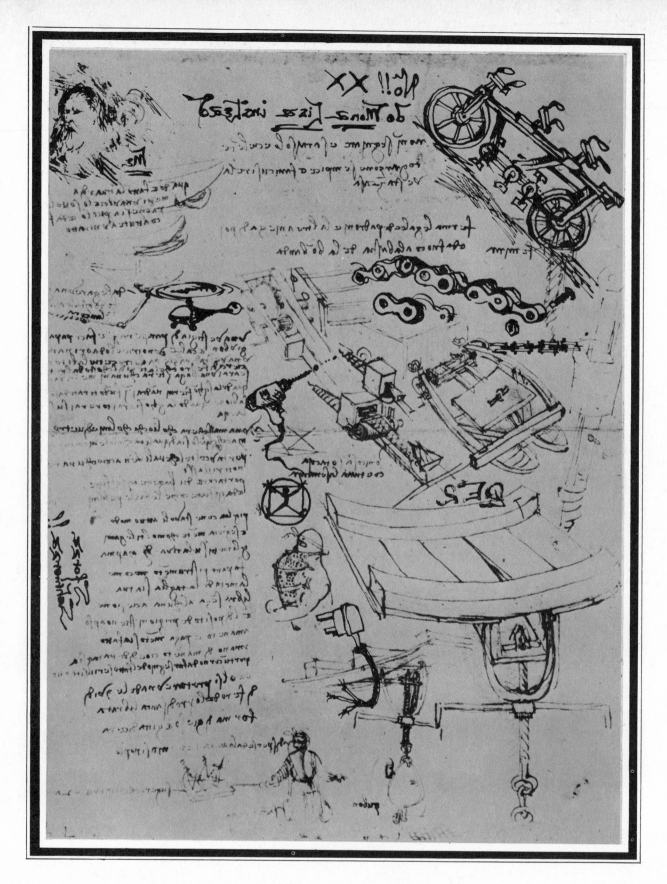

Sketch by Leonardo da Vinci (pinched from Windsor Collection).

Hope dis·a da sorta ting
you want
                  uv Pablo

300 Honours

How would you like an *OBE*?

Like to be called *SIR*?

Fancy yourself as a *DAME* of the British Empire?

If your answer to any of these questions is **"NOT 'ARF"**, just fill in the form – cut it out – and send it to:

**NEW YEAR'S HONOURS
HER MAJESTY
BUCKINGHAM PALACE
(Opposite St James' Park)
LONDON**

All you have to do is tick the award and tell us why you think you should get it (in not more than five words, not less than four).

BEFORE

AFTER

And how about this:

If you apply for more than 3 Honours, we will send you — at NO EXTRA COST — a copy of . . .

THIS MAGNIFICENT LIMITED EDITION

Bound in real Butler-skin!
They'll look great on your bookshelves.

"Scóne" or "Scŏne"?
"Crumpet" or "Pikelet"?
"Lunch" or "Dinner"? Which is "correct"?
"Room" or "Rum"?
"Toilet" or "Lavvy"?

This is the actual manual as used by Royal Nannies to instruct generations of regal infants in the art of speaking proper. It has become THE standard handbook for developing the "correct" vocabulary of . . . Lady Show-jumpers, Conservative MP's, BBC Newsreaders, and all nicely spoken people.

Now it can be yours-

absolutely FREE!

179 volumes- they look great

IT'S ALL IN "THE QUEEN'S ENGLISH"

*Bookshelves available NOW – £s per foot – write for details
SPECIAL OFFER

Suddenly all the birds fancy me! Dame Reginald Platt OBE

must be won

NO SKILL/TALENT REQUIRED ● FANTASTIC GIVE-AWAY OFFER

EVERYBODY'S DOING IT!

...otballers, Pop-singers, Disc-jockeys – even ...z musicians! These days, everybody – and ...NYBODY – seems to have some kind of ...onour". So why should YOU be left out? ...ere was a time when you had to have ...rformed some great service to the nation ...e inviting princess Margaret to tea every ...her Sunday) but NOT ANY MORE. Now, ...last, NEW YEAR'S HONOURS are to be ...de available to people like YOU. And what ...difference it will make to YOUR life, if you ...t one.

WHAT A DIFFERENCE!

...e GUARANTEE that YOU will suddenly ...d out what it is like to be RESPECTED.

SUDDENLY...

...raffic Wardens will turn a blind eye when ...OU park YOUR Rolls-Royce on the yellow ...e.
...OU can razz up the M1 at *any speed you* ...e!
...ank loans become *"No Problem"*.
...hopkeepers will knock *"a bit off"* at the ...erest whisper of those magic letters . . .
. . . B . . . E . . . !

...UT DON'T TAKE OUR WORD FOR IT. FIND OUT FOR YOURSELF!

...hy not take advantage of our special limited ...fer of a free PLASTIC REPLICA OBE? ...ent, on approval, for two weeks, at absolutely ...o cost to YOURSELF. (Warning – on the ...th day the "OBE" will self-destruct, so ...LEASE make sure YOU are not wearing it).

OR ARE YOU ALREADY CONVINCED?

...n that case, no need to bother with the plastic ...eplica – just fill in the form and get THE ...EAL THING, by return of post.

AND WHY STOP AT ONE?

...here is NO LIMIT to the number of ...onours YOU can possess (provided YOUR ...pplication is made through this advertise- ...ent). Make no mistake about it, the more ...tters YOU have after YOUR name, the more ...spect YOU'LL get – and the more YOUR ...iends will envy YOU!

...ules of the Competition:
...o Cheating
...embers of the Royal Family may not enter

YOUR CHOICE: Silver, gold, re-inforced plastic or fibre glass.

FUNNY HAT Free to every entrant

CHOICE of fur, ermine, fox, gorilla, bandicoot or bushbaby.

Plus THESE INSTRUCTIONAL RECORDS

How to talk Posh

which will enable YOU to lose once and for all YOUR embarrassing local dialect, and replace it with a nice upper-class accent. FEATURING: the voices of: Analie Drummond-Hay, Lady Isobel Barnett, Brian Clough, and special "Mystery Guest".

AVAILABLE with platform heels.

CHOICE OF COLOURS Blue, red, prune or "poo-poo".

DON'T DELAY–FILL THE FORM TO-DAY!

I THINK I OUGHT TO BE A KNIGHT/DAME/LORD/ OWNER OF AN OBE/MBE/ANYTHING ELSE/BECAUSE:

_____

_____

Signed:

Address:

I agree to abide by the rules of the competition*.
I do not already possess an Honour.
If I get an Honour, I agree to pay £10,000 per annum to the Royal Family Benevolent Fund (or the equivalent in champagne, horses, polo-mallets etc).
I enclose SAE and 50p postage and packing (75p for a Dukedom).
PLEASE ALSO SEND ME FREE MY COPY OF "THE QUEEN'S ENGLISH", PLUS INSTRUCTIONAL RECORDS "HOW TO TALK POSH", PLUS FREE FUNNY HAT. ☐ Tick for details of bookshelves

PLEASE SEND ME EXPLODING PLASTIC REPLICA OBE ON 14 DAYS APPROVAL.
I realize that you accept no liability for damage/injury/death etc.

Signed:

Address:

OR

Mrs E. Tole.
(Biographer - Researcher -
Informer - Snout.)

...here Books esq°

...ar Gents,
Well! The trouble I had to go
...to get this!! I know you wanted
...hat you called some juicy bits to
...ive the "File" a good ending, but
...hy I couldnt' just make up a pack
...f lies I do not know. Anyway I
...nicked this lot from Nancy Bottle...'
Scrapbook, which was not easy
...tell you. He came in just as...
...luckily mistook me for...
pantomime dromeday. For...
I just hope you...
worth it, and
one million

·NOT· TO BE TAKEN ·AWAY·

...o Bailey Official Court Records

the case of

The Metropolitan Police v The so-called self styled clever-dick GOODIES

date 15th November 1974

Safely received,
Stanley, petal.
Le
Bless You!
x

George
Bottle of the Yard

N.B. This is THE official record of
this case. There is one copy, and
one copy only, and THIS is it. It
is the PROPERTY OF THE OLD BAILEY
CASE LIBRARY. The Library is open
on TUES, WEDS and SATS (CLOSED AT
HALF TERM, BANK HOLS AND IF CHELSEA
ARE AT HOME) For REFERENCE only.
The information herein is confidential,
secret, and you shouldn't really be
reading it.

Stan Ographer (CLERK)

CLERK:

DAY ONE

It was a nice sunny morning when we all assembled in Number One Court. We watched
Rod Laver beat Ken Rosewall in straight sets. Then we all moved to Number Two
Court to get on with the case of THE METROPOLITAN POLICE V THE GOODIES. The judge
was our very old friend Justice Once. At first he seemed overcome by the
seriousness of the matter before him, and he was broody and silent. He then fell
off his chair and was discovered to be, in fact, dead. A doctor confirmed that
Justice Once had been in this condition for several months, but saw no reason why
he should not continue with his duties. There was, however, an objection from the
substitute bench, and the corpse was replaced by the first Pygmy Judge to sit on
the Queens Bench (most of them are too little to reach). His name was Justice
Ongat Wilite (laughter in court). The judge banged his gavel but the doctor
applied a soothing ointment and he then introduced the case.

He explained that charges were to be brought against THE GOODIES by P.C. BENT
of the Metropolitan Police. The Police case was to be conducted by the firm of
BOOTS, BOOTS, BOOTS, BOOTS, MARCHINUP AND DOWNAGAIN (Solicitors). However,
Mr. Boots was indisposed and had arranged that his place should be taken by
Mr. Boots. Mr. Boots was, alas, rather nervous and was throwing up in the loo,
and it was, therefore, agreed that Mr. Boots should deputise, until it was
discovered that he was on holiday. The fourth Mr. Boots was apparently a typist's
error, and Marchinup and Downagain were merely a silly joke thought up by the
first Mr. Boots. The prosecution was eventually conducted by MR. IZZY BENT Q.C.
(former theatrical agent, and no relation to P.C. BENT).

THE GOODIES asked for Legal Aid, but were told that it had all gone, and
they had to make do with Lemon Aid. They elected to conduct their own defence,
for reasons of poverty.

THE JURY were then selected, and consisted of MR. NATHANIEL BENT (CHAIRMAN),
JEREMY AND ALOYSIUS BENT, THE BENT TWINS, COLONEL ARTHUR BENT, THE REVEREND
PHYLLIS BENT AND THE FIVE "TUMBLING" BENT BROTHERS. (All no relations).

Each member of the Jury raised his right hand, and they were all allowed
to leave the room.

MR. IZZY BENT (PROSECUTION) was then asked to name the charges brought against
the so-called self-styled clever-dick GOODIES. MR. BENT consulted his client
(MR. BENT). He then told the court that he couldn't really think of anything off
hand, but he was fairly sure that THE GOODIES were likely to do something
extremely naughty any minute. He appealed to the Judge to bring back hanging.

The Judge declared that he would adjourn the hearing for two days to give
MR. BENT time to think up some really damning charges. He also appealed to the
JURY to help MR. BENT think up something; and he appealed to THE GOODIES to do
something criminal, which would, he said, make the case a lot easier.

                              COURT ADJOURNED

DAY TWO

Still thinking

DAY THREE

This morning began with MR. BENT (PROSECUTING) bringing the following charges against THE GOODIES.

1: That they did issue a libellous statement against one MRS. E. TOLE, to wit; that: "This woman is a good for nothing old rat bag."

2: They did it again.

3: They might well do it yet again.

4: They are directly responsible for the rising cost of petrol.

5: They are directly responsible for the rising cost of everything else.

6: They masterminded the Watergate cover up.

7: They persuaded the BBC to do a second series of "FROST'S WEEKLY" (boos in court).

8: They started the French Revolution.

9: They discovered America.

The Judge reminded MR. BENT that all these allegations must be proved BEYOND ALL REASONABLE DOUBT. After consulting his client, MR. BENT decided to withdraw the last six charges.

THE GOODIES pleaded GUILTY to the charges of libel, repeated libel and intended repeated libel, but claimed it was FAIR COMMENT.

MR. BROOKE TAYLOR assured the court that he would call many witnesses who would testify to the good name of THE GOODIES. These would include SHEIK AHMED EL FATA, MR. EDWARD HEATH, MR. RICHARD NIXON, MR. DAVID FROST, CARDINAL RICHELIEU and CHRISTOPHER COLUMBUS.

At this point the Judge asked THE GOODIES if they had a criminal record. They replied (not surprisingly) that they indeed possessed an LP of LITTLE JIMMY OSMOND. It was played. MR. OSMOND was sentenced to ten years hard labour (ON THE MAX BYGRAVES SHOW).

COURT ADJOURNED

DAY FOUR

THE PROSECUTION

MR. BENT today opened his case. He took out his sandwiches, and closed it again. He then asked MRS. E. TOLE to take the witness box. She did so, but the Judge made her put it back. MR. BENT then began his cross-examination of MRS. TOLE, which is here transcribed in full.

BENT:	Your name is MRS. EDNA TOLE.
MRS. TOLE:	Yes, I know it is.
BENT:	Would you please tell the court, Mrs. Tole, are you a good for nothing old rat bag?
MRS. TOLE:	Yes. (Laughter in court).
BENT:	(Very slowly) I am going to ask you that question again, and this time I want you to think very carefully, and take as long as you like before answering. Are you, Mrs. Tole, a good for nothing old rat bag?

COURT ADJOURNED

MRS. TOLE:	...... Yes.
BENT:	I'm sorry M'Lord but I've forgotten the question.
JUDGE:	I think Mrs. Tole meant to say "No" ... Is that right Mrs. Tole?
MRS. TOLE:	Yes.
BENT:	So! You deny it?
MRS. TOLE:	Yes.
BENT:	And would you tell the court please what you, in fact, ARE?
MRS. TOLE:	Yes.
BENT:	WHAT are you?
MRS. TOLE:	I am a good for nothing old rat bag.
BENT:	You see M'Lord she answers with a modesty that surely testifies to her excellence of character; and how these nasty foul-mouthed, so-called GOODIES could libel her so wickedly, I do not know!
MR. BROOKE TAYLOR:	But M'Lord Mrs. Tole has just admitted that she is indeed a good for nothing old rat bag.
BENT:	She is also a dotty old crone who doesn't know what she's talking about and I submit, M'Lord, that her testimony is totally untrustworthy.
JUDGE:	I agree. Mrs. Tole strikes me as a loony.
MRS. TOLE:	Thank you sir.

SO ENDED THE CASE FOR THE PROSECUTION

COURT ADJOURNED

DAY EIGHT

THE DEFENCE

MR. BROOKE TAYLOR (DEFENDING) today began his defence of the defendants.

MR. BROOKE TAYLOR:	M'Lud I shall now prove that, on the night in question, myself and my colleagues were, in fact, at a "party" in the private rooms of a gent of some public standing, and, what's more, you can't touch us for it. I call my first witness: Chief Inspector George Bottle.
MR. BROOKE TAYLOR:	You are Chief Inspector George Bottle, and you are, I believe, also known as "Nancy".
BOTTLE:	Takes one to know one, chubbycheeks.
MR. BROOKE TAYLOR:	Nancy ... would you tell us please what you were doing on the night in question?

BOTTLE:	Well YOU should know that, sweetie pie ... <u>wasn't</u> it fun?
JUDGE:	Will you please answer the question Mr. Bottle?
BOTTLE:	Oh come on, I don't have to tell YOU, Sugardrawers... you can't have forgotten <u>already</u>!
BENT:	Are you implying that his Lordship was present at this "party"?
BOTTLE:	Well <u>you</u> saw him, didn't you?
BENT:	Er... that is for the Jury to decide.
JURY:	We saw him!
MR. BROOKE TAYLOR:	Quite a party wasn't it?
ALL:	Yes!
MR. BROOKE TAYLOR:	Now, I put it to you, Mr. Bottle, that certain <u>other</u> people were also present at this "party", whom, for reasons of security, I shall refer to as Mr. A, Mr. B, Sheik C, The Right Honorable D, President E, Cardinal F, Mr. G, Sir H, and Tortoise I. Is that correct?
BOTTLE:	Almost, petal. In fact Mr. B was out burying his granny, but Mister K, L and M were there too, and so was Mr. or Mrs. N ... I'm STILL not sure about him, are you?... anyway ... oh yes, and the Tortoise was X, not I.
MR. BROOKE TAYLOR:	And I believe certain photographs were taken of these certain people?
BOTTLE:	I should say SO, cheeky chops!
	THE CERTAIN PHOTOGRAPHS WERE THEN PASSED ROUND THE COURT. THEY ARE HERE ATTACHED.

DAY NINE

STILL LOOKING AT PHOTOGRAPHS

DAY TEN AND ELEVEN

STILL LOOKING

DAY TWELVE

The day began with the Court in uproar as MR. BROOKE TAYLOR called his key witnesses; MISTERS A, G and K, SHEIK C, THE RIGHT HON. D, PRESIDENT E and CARDINAL F. So that their faces should not be recognised, they appeared in the guise of a six-legged Pantomime Dromedary, who was then cross examined thus:

MR. BROOKE TAYLOR:	You are Misters A, G, K, Sheik C, The Right Honorable D, President E and Cardinal F?
DROMEDARY:	Yes.
MR. BROOKE TAYLOR:	Could you tell the court, do you see anyone here today whom you would describe as a good for nothing old rat bag?
DROMEDARY:	Yes.

MR. BROOKE TAYLOR: Would you point to that person, please?

The Dromedary then pointed to the Judge, two members of the Jury, Chief Inspector Bottle, and - crucial evidence, this - MRS. E. TOLE. In doing so, the animal occupied five of its six legs, and fell over. THE GOODIES helped it up.

DROMEDARY: Thank you. And whilst I'm at it, I would also like to thank you, and your colleagues, for negotiating my oil deal, for trying to work out my anti-inflationary policy, for editing my tape, for getting me another series, for defeating the Huguenots and for piloting the Santa Maria.

GOODIES: Lies, all lies!

                                    COURT ADJOURNED

DAY THIRTEEN

THE VERDICT

THE JURY FOUND THE GOODIES "GUILTY" ON ALL NINE CHARGES.

THE SENTENCES

JUDGE: Goodies, I am sure you <u>are</u>, in fact, guilty of this libellous statement against MRS. TOLE, but then so is everyone else, so it doesn't count.

                     Also, though you are apparently guilty of the other six charges, MR. BENT saw fit to withdraw them on the first day, so they don't count either. Therefore, I cannot pass sentence on you, which is a pity because I am in an ingenious mood and I had thought up some very amusing punishments ... never mind.

                     Finally, I would like to remind everyone in this courtroom that what you have heard during the past thirteen days is of the upmost secrecy. Some of the revelations uncovered during this hearing have been to say the least, sensational.

                     I fully realise that some sneaky, unprincipled, enterprising publishers could very easily make a great deal of money if they got their hands on some of this fascinating information.

                     (CRIES OF "SHAME", "HOW <u>COULD</u> THEY" AND "OVER MY DEAD BODY")

                     If this does happen ... I shall be extremely cross ... if I do not get my usual rake off. The case is now closed.

BOTTLE: May I have my photos back?

JUDGE: No.

                                    COURT ADJOURNED

                          Stan Ographer (CLERK)
                          Feb. 1974.

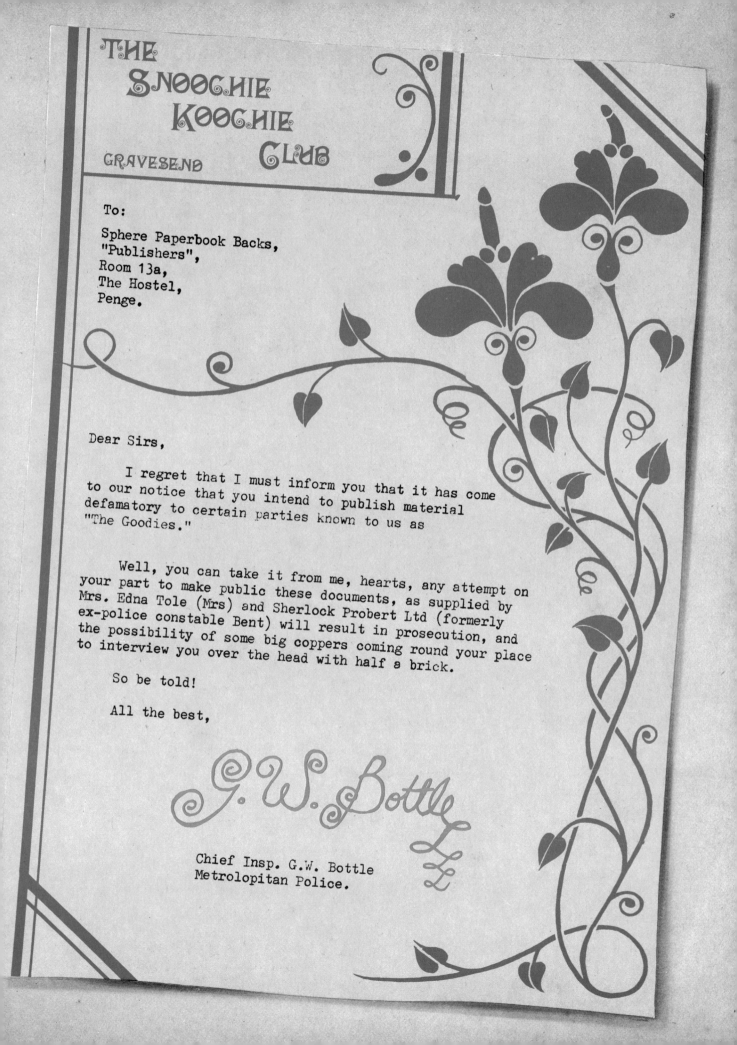

THE SNOOCHIE KOOCHIE CLUB

GRAVESEND

To:

Sphere Paperbook Backs,
"Publishers",
Room 13a,
The Hostel,
Penge.

Dear Sirs,

I regret that I must inform you that it has come
to our notice that you intend to publish material
defamatory to certain parties known to us as
"The Goodies."

Well, you can take it from me, hearts, any attempt on
your part to make public these documents, as supplied by
Mrs. Edna Tole (Mrs) and Sherlock Probert Ltd (formerly
ex-police constable Bent) will result in prosecution, and
the possibility of some big coppers coming round your place
to interview you over the head with half a brick.

So be told!

All the best,

G. W. Bottle

Chief Insp. G.W. Bottle
Metrolopitan Police.

Sphere Books Limited
30·32 Gray's Inn Road,
London WC1X 8JL
(Registered Office)

Telephone: 01-405 6683 (6 lines)
 01-405 2087 (4 lines)
Telegrams and Cables:
Spherbooks London WC1

A subsidiary of the
Thomson Organisation Limited.
ABACUS: CARDINAL: SPHERE.

If we don't answer try the Acme Transport Cafe on the corner.

to: Chief Inspector "Nancy" Bottle,
 c/o the Metrolopitan Police,
 (or try 'Cecil's' in Brewer St.,)
 LONDON
 ENGLAND
 Nr France.

Today.

Dear Chief Inspector Bottle,

We were deeply concerned to receive your recent communication regarding our intended publication of "The Goodies File".

Of course we had not realised the severe implications of our actions, such as the big policemen coming round our place etc.

We can only reassure you that, in view of these circumstances, we shall of course go no further with this venture.
Moreover we dissociate ourselves totally from the dubious activities of Mrs Edna Tole (Mrs) and ex-P.c. Bent (Now Gladys and Partner, amazing stunts with a Combine Harvester, and a great success too we might add!) Our only defence in the circumstances is that we were prepared to accept P.c. Bent's evidence as reliable, as his father, Hector Bent, is an old friend of ours, and I gather carries some weight in your organisation.

It now appears we have been sadly deceived, and wishing no harm to come to your colleagues The Goodies, we give you our solemn word that we have no intention of publishing the aforementioned work. *This is true.*
(Legal Dept.)

Furthermore, we promise not to publish it.

In conclusion, it is definitely not our intention to publish the facts made known to us.

Even if we did publish them, we probably wouldn't make the money we expected anyway. So we won't. Promise.

Honestly, we aren't going to publish the Goodies File.

Really and truly.

So there it is. We must meet for a drink sometime.

Yours

P. T. O.

Directors: Basil Sphere (Chairman), Hymie Sphere (Chief Executive),
G. Sphere, M. Sphere, B. M. Sphere, G. M. Sphere, G. Sphere, D. D.,
Oy—Vay Sphere, M. Sphere, D. D. Sphere, Z. Sphere, A. B. Sphere,
B. M. Sphere, B. F. Sphere, M. Sphere.

cheers!
Basil Sphere, Don and all the gang

Printed at Sphere paperbook backs

Currently at the Alhambra, Stoke

Top Secret

HANDS OFF!

CONFIDENTIAL

BRITISH ARMY INTELLIGENCE
"Dunpeepin"
Edgbaston
Nr. Omsk

19.10.74

Dear Mrs Tole,

I am returning the enclosed Dossier on 'The Goodies' which
you so kindly sent, as I am afraid it is of no immediate interest
to us. Nor indeed could we consider paying you the sum of one
million pounds that you mention, although we do appreciate your
remarks on the current price of butter.
Suggest you try elsewhere - the Chinese might be interested.

Regards

Major Eyes-Water.

Major Eyes-Water

CONFIDENTIAL

HANDS OFF!!

NO NO NO!

Sorry - no use to us
Admiral T. Arch
Naval Intelligence

Load Off Rubbish!
Wingko Zeppelin
RAF Spying Dept.

Oh come on!
Elizabeth R

Return to sender.
M Suggs (Mr.)
East Peter Scout Polise.

Try News of the World
yours Sunday People

Try Sunday People
Yrs. News of the World
You've just tried us
ys. Sunday People.

No thankyou
Auntie.
N.O.W. love to uncle Pop
Ethel E Stan X

Might just be something
here I could use.
Bless you!!!
D. Froo

Wen don't send it back to us